# Total Quality in General Practice

**Provided as an educational service by**

# Total Quality in General Practice

## Practical steps to implementing the Patient's Charter

### Jacqueline Brooks

Specialist in Health Services Management,
Hadzor Health Consultants

and

### Irene Borgardts

Chief Executive, Oxfordshire Family Health Services Authority

With a Foreword by

**Sir Donald Irvine**

General Practitioner, Ashington, Northumberland,
and Regional Adviser in General Practice,
University of Newcastle upon Tyne

Radcliffe Medical Press
Oxford and New York

© 1994 Radcliffe Medical Press Ltd
18 Marcham Road, Abingdon, Oxon, OX14 1AA, UK

Radcliffe Medical Press, Inc.
141 Fifth Avenue, New York, NY 10010, USA

Reprinted 1995

British Library Cataloguing in Publication Data

A catalogue record for this book is available from the British Library.


ISBN 1 85775 066 7

Typeset by Tradespools
Printed and bound in Great Britain

# CONTENTS

# FOREWORD

It is good to see the quality movement in British general practice gaining steadily in momentum. It was a handful of enthusiastic members of the Royal College of General Practitioners who led the way in the 1970s, to be followed in the early 1980s by the College's Quality Initiative, which sought to extend quality assurance to every practice. This voluntary professional programme was given further impetus in the Health Reforms when the government decided that clinical audit should become part of all NHS general practice. Even more recently, leading edge practices have begun to explore the relevance and application of Total Quality Management to our sector of the health service.

This book describes one such innovatory approach. The Hereford and Worcester Family Health Services Authority initiated and supervised the experiment, in which four volunteer general practices submitted themselves to external review, including an appraisal of their services by their patients. The writers record the essential experiences and lessons from this splendid example of teamwork between managers and practices, at the sharp end of health care.

The book focuses on management methods, emphasizing in particular the central functions of planning, standard setting and performance monitoring, to practices which are keen to improve and to move forward at a pace, and in a way that members of the practice team can handle without feeling pressured or overworked. Inevitably, the emphasis is on the environment for care and the arrangements for care which rely on effective administration. The integration of clinical standard setting and performance monitoring is not attempted, but the reader is left with more than a hint of how this might be done. Here, perhaps, is a book for another day!

The book will appeal both to the clinical and non-clinical members of the practice team, and should prove equally valuable to those in health services management who are interested in promoting quality in primary health care. The participating practices became known as 'Pathfinders for Excellence'. In the chapters which follow, we learn just how they earned that deserved reputation.

Sir Donald Irvine
*February 1994*

# PREFACE

In the Summer of 1991, Hereford and Worcester Family Health Services Authority (FHSA) invited local general practices to become involved in a new project to implement what was termed a 'total quality initiative' in their own surgeries.

In essence, this was an opportunity for them to review a variety of aspects of their practice, with the help of outside consultants.

At a workshop in September 1991, it was agreed that there would be four participating practices, who became known as 'pathfinders for excellence', – a term felt to be more digestible than the original 'total quality' label!

With some trepidation, the four volunteers submitted themselves to both an independent consumer survey, carried out by a second outside consultancy firm to ensure objectivity, and a 'health-check' review, by the main consultants – Hadzor Health Consultants.

The aim of the health-check phase is described in detail in the following pages. However, the main objective was to identify the practices' current strengths and weaknesses – in other words a position statement. Once this information was to hand, they could decide, having received a detailed report from the Hadzor Court Team, which issues they wished to tackle with consultancy help.

The result was that two of the practices went ahead with a full business plan, with help at key intervals. For example, one of these practices decided to have a series of business planning seminars for the partners and practice manager.

A third practice concentrated on its systems and procedures, and the fourth asked for further assistance with developing the role of its primary health care team, which it saw as fundamental to the future effectiveness of its programme of care.

The FHSA itself, who became the fifth pilot, took a more traditional 'total quality' approach, appropriate to larger organizations, and set up departmental Quality Improvement Groups to monitor the services both to contractors and between sections of its own organization.

The Pathfinder Project process perfectly anticipated the Patient's Charter, and thus has become a very practical model to be used in the implementation of Charter issues.

All of the participants in the Pathfinder Project enjoyed the activity and, without exception, found the view of an outside firm invaluable. In describing the advantages, the most frequently stated comment was that the report of the consultants had acted as a catalyst – sometimes proving to be just the required stimulation to tackle problems that were already known, but had been left in abeyance.

As a result of the degree of interest shown by general practices in the initial Pathfinders for Excellence Project, and in view of the Patient's Charter, Hereford and Worcester and the Hadzor consultants developed a Total Quality Kit, which has subsequently given rise to this book.

Parties who decide to pursue a Total Quality Initiative (TQI) will find they need outside assistance for the analytic of 'health-check' phase. Participating practices will benefit also from the support of their Primary Care Facilitators.

We hope you will enjoy using this book – we know from experience that practices find TQI is a worthwhile exercise and that, just by taking part in the process, practices can greatly enhance their team-working.

# INTRODUCTION:

# How to Use this Book

This book is designed to allow practices flexibility in introducing aspects of total quality that are appropriate to their circumstances whilst, at the same time, giving them sufficient information to undertake a full-scale programme should they wish to do so. It keeps the Patient's Charter in view at all times, but also goes much further into the methods of achieving harmonious working of the practice team.

There are five main sections to the book. Each section consists of one or more chapters on specific topics.

Section A gives general background information and outlines the importance of the Patient's Charter.

Section B explains how to seek the views of patients and practice partners and staff in confirming the practice's current strengths and weaknesses. To do this, it uses three methods of securing general information – each of which should help to reinforce the picture of the practice as it is now. These three methods include Patient (Consumer) Survey, SWOT (Strengths, Weaknesses, Opportunities and Threats) Analysis and finally, semi-structured interviews. You will need outside assistance to perform some of these effectively, and may find the Primary Care Facilitators particularly helpful in these circumstances.

By the end of Section B, you should have a fairly clear idea where the practice's priorities should lie in terms of changes which it may need to make.

Section C gives help in reviewing specific areas of the practice. These include quality in organizational culture and management style, the physical environment, and quality in systems and procedures.

Almost certainly your practice needs will fall to a greater or lesser degree into each of these three main areas, but where to put the main emphasis is the choice of each individual practice, in the implementation of local standards of the Patient's Charter.

Section D explains how to measure the effectiveness of what the practice does. It provides a blueprint for deciding what are the most important aspects of the practice activities (key results areas), and discusses how to set standards and targets to ensure the results are being achieved, giving examples from the Patient's Charter.

Section E, the final section, is on 'next steps', which outlines the option of developing a full business plan for your practice. Total quality links well with a business plan, and it is a logical step to develop the services your practice provides in a business planning framework.

For further information and advice contact: – Jacqueline B. Brooks, Lead Consultant, Hadzor Health Consultants, Hadzor Court, Droitwich Spa, Worcestershire WR9 7DR; Tel: (0905) 794401.

# SECTION A

# Background Information

# CHAPTER 1

# A Brief Outline of Total Quality

## Background to Quality Control

The concept of checking quality has been around for a very long time. Obvious examples are the hallmarks on gold and silver, and, of course, the British Standards 'kite' marks.

Although it was originally the end product that was checked, this proved to be an extremely expensive operation, and so it developed into a system of checking the *process* of manufacture. In other words, if the systems and procedures were correct, the end product would, by definition, also be of a high standard.

Some names, for example, W Edwards Deming, Joseph N Juran, and Phillip B Crosby, have become synonymous with 'Total Quality Management'[1]. Although they have different approaches, the common thread is their belief that there are no short cuts to quality and that the improvement process is on-going – not a one-off exercise. It requires the full participation of everyone – from individuals to the most senior people in the organization.

[1] The terms 'total quality management' (TQM), and 'total quality initiative' (TQI), are both used in the text. TQI should be read as the process by which TQM is introduced, ie a Total Quality Initiative is the action taken to implement Total Quality Management.

## What Exactly is Total Quality Management?

The basic premise in Total Quality Management (TQM) is that everyone is a supplier to someone else – not purely to the end user. Quality is an on-going process which can fail at any stage in this chain of customer–supplier. For example, a cook may provide the wrong meal to the end customer if the waiter has given him an inaccurate order. Therefore, the cook is the internal customer of the waiter, and the end customer receives poor quality service because the quality chain has been broken. Some examples of this concept of the internal customer in a general practice setting are given later in this chapter.

Thus, a very important part of Total Quality is to ensure that everyone is aware of how their performance has an effect on satisfying the end customer's needs – total quality firms motivate their staff (and their suppliers) to ensure there is a consistent delivery of quality.

The main features of Total Quality are the same for every organization, whether it is a large commericial concern, a hospital or general practice. However, with commercial companies there is bound to be an emphasis on cost savings – in financial terms – by improved techniques. For general practices, the main reasons for entering the total quality environment appear to be more related to improved efficiency (less hassle) and the 'people' areas of TQM – having a happy, motivated workforce, and ensuring they do not lose patients from their lists.

## BS5750

BS5750 is often confused with Total Quality. In fact, BS5750 is the national standard for quality systems. BS5750 was first published in 1979 and has since spread throughout industry, and more recently into the health service – including general practice.

The emphasis of BS5750 is on establishing and maintaining an effective quality system, ie the product or service is designed and delivered in a way which satisfies customer needs. BS5750 is therefore about systems, and firms implementing it have to:

■ say what they do

■ say why they do it

4

- do what they say they will do

- record what they actually did

BS5750 relies on control in every aspect of the firm's operation. Its aim is to prevent error – not trying to put things right after the event. Its approach is to apply a systematic approach to every activity which contributes to the end product or service, having first identified its customers' needs.

This systematic approach can be a good starting point for someone who wishes to begin the process of Total Quality. However, Total Quality is people-led, it is about leadership from the top, empowerment of individuals, with the actual standard being just one part of the process. The attitude of individuals makes the achievement of the standard more likely.

BS5750 and Total Quality can fit together well. Total Quality brings in more 'people' orientation – rather than being purely a systematic approach. Total Quality involves a culture or philosophy about how things should work. In BS5750, the goal is simply to meet the standard set. In Total Quality, the theme is ongoing improvement, with total employee involvement and commitment which often requires attitude change (*see* Chapter 4). Teamwork, without which a general practice cannot function, is a prime feature of Total Quality and TQM is therefore a particularly appropriate model for standards in general practice.

## Measurement and Costs

There is a cost to implementing Total Quality. The costs of not implementing it, however, are usually greater. The cost of making mistakes, for example the cost of the time spent in looking for misfiles, re-making appointments, re-working letters because of earlier mistakes etc, should all be quantified as a cost of not having a quality system.

The costs of having a quality system also need to be quantified. They include the failure costs and failing to achieve the specified standard, which includes management time in putting things right (this is usually a hidden or unquantified cost where no quality system exists). There are also the evaluation or monitoring costs. These involve monitoring to see whether the quality standard is being achieved, for example a supervisor checking delivery times where a standard for this has been specified. In

5

general practice, it may involve the senior receptionist surveying the length of time patients wait in the surgery after arrival before they are seen.

Finally, there are the costs of prevention. These include the costs of the action taken to analyse the cause of failure to meet the agreed standard and to tighten up the quality system to prevent mistakes happening again. The total is usually referred to as the Total Quality Cost.

General practices should not overlook the *opportunity costs*. For example, if a practice nurse has been given the wrong information on her appointments list and has a gap at an unexpected time of day but a long backlog of double bookings at the end, then the opportunity cost is the option she has lost to use that time more effectively on some other activity.

## Quality in Health Care

It may seem easy, and even appropriate, to apply Total Quality to manufacturing or production, but just how do we define quality in terms of general practice?

Quality in clinical outcomes, relying as it does on the individual doctor/patient relationship, does not lend itself readily to a Total Quality Initiative.

The aim of this book is not to prescribe for this crucial doctor/patient relationship in terms of clinical procedures. That is the remit of practice protocols and medical audit and is already monitored separately by FHSAs. It is assumed, therefore, that the practice aims will include the following.

- Appropriateness of treatment and care.

- Achievement of optimum clinical outcome.

- Clinically recognized procedures to minimize complications and similar preventable events.

Having established that these areas are the prime function of general practice, how can a Total Quality Initiative ensure that the supporting functions are as effective as possible, in order to facilitate its prime purpose of patient care?

The essential functions of these supporting features in the practice are included in the Patient's Charter. In summary, they are:

6

- an attitude that treats patients with dignity and as individuals

- an environment conducive to patient safety, reassurance and contentment

- speed of response to patient needs and minimum inconvenience to them.

All key result[2] areas and related standards should help to fulfil these essential features.

Quality Standards in the supporting areas can be divided loosely into two parts: (1) the efficiency and effectiveness of the services; and (2) the underlying staff morale.

The two are unavoidably interlinked and together contribute to Total Quality. A good standard and style of staff management is essential in creating the environment (the organizational culture) for achieving quality in patient services. It simply is not possible to 'graft' the Patient's Charter Standards onto a dissatisfied or demoralized workforce. This book therefore considers how to develop a highly motivated workforce as a *foundation* for implementing excellence in service provision as described by the Patient's Charter. In other words, it provides a *practical* approach to adapting Total Quality Management to running a general practice.

The following chapters describe these areas in more depth.


## The Main Features of Total Quality in a General Practice

Once a Total Quality programme has been initiated, it should demonstrate the following characteristics.

- It will have the support of the GP partners – the leadership must come from the most senior level.

- It will involve the whole practice, including all sections of work and every individual.

- It will accept that the achievement of good quality is everyone's responsibility – even those who do not deal directly with patients or other 'customers'.

[2] For an explanation of 'key results' see Chapter 7, p.65.

- Everyone in the practice will have a customer or client for the work that they do. This brings in the concept of the 'internal customer' (explained in more depth on page 9).

- The practice environment will be one where the likelihood of mistakes and problems is minimized. The aim is prevention, not simply identification and blame after a problem or mistake has occurred.

- Each part of the service in a general practice will have identified its most important functions. We refer to these most important aspects as 'key result areas'. These key result areas have measurable standards set, below which the service will not fall. This is usually referred to as hitting the target 'first time, every time'.

- The theme in the practice will be one of continuous improvement, in the belief that any process in running the practice can be improved upon at any given time.

To implement Total Quality successfully, there are some prerequisites. If these are not in place, then any attempt to set standards is likely to fail. It is during the health-check* phase that the current situation of the practice in relation to these aspects is assessed. These are:

- absolute commitment and leadership from the partners, as mentioned earlier

- a positive organizational culture (explained in Chapter 4), which involves having an agreed philosophy for the practice, based on shared values that are understood by all staff.

The establishment of these prerequisites is the most difficult part of Total Quality Management, because they may well require attitude change, and/or a change in the way the practice is managed, together with a real acceptance that everyone is working towards the same goals.

---

* 'health-check' – The initial analytical phase of a Total Quality Initiative, which asks ''Where are we now?''

## Who are our 'Customers'?

The concept of the customer is integral to a Total Quality approach. Customers may be external or internal.

*External customers* are all those who are not employed by the practice. Therefore, the practice's external customers would include, for example, patients, Family Health Services Authorities (FHSAs), and hospitals.

The practice's *internal customers* would include staff, most of whom, in their turn, would be relying on other staff to help them fulfil the service to the external customer.

For example, a receptionist may require the general practitioners to sign prescriptions rapidly so that the patient's script is ready when he or she arrives to collect it. In this example, the receptionist is the internal customer of the GP.

Similarly, the partners will require their appointment systems to work effectively if they are to have the notes readily available for the correct patient. In this case, the partners are the internal customers of the receptionist whose role it is to prepare the surgeries.

**KEY POINT – Total Quality relies on excellent teamwork**

Everyone in the practice is working ultimately to fulfil the needs of the end customer, ie the patient. Satisfying the needs of the internal customer is a vital interim step. Individuals need to help each other to perform their role well to the overall benefit of the practice.

## The Benefits of a Total Quality Initiative

Implementing Total Quality brings many benefits. These include:

- the opportunity to provide an efficient and effective service to patients

- co-operation – rather than conflict – and enhancement of teamwork

- greater involvement of all staff in decision-making

- shared, agreed, and properly understood standards and targets

- fewer mistakes

- opportunities for job enrichment and creative thinking.

Interestingly, results usually are obvious long before the initial Total Quality Review is completed. This is because the process of seeking staff views, asking them to review their systems and checking how they feel about their work, in itself tends to increase morale in the practice. This is known as a 'Hawthorne Effect'.[3]

Morale is heightened by a positive, open management style, which in turn leads staff to feel enthusiastic about their own responsibilities.

## Conclusion

In summary, therefore, total quality has two main threads:

1 Quality in management standards.

2 Quality in setting standards for the services provided.

The combination of these is the foundation for TQM, with quality in management standards facilitating the organizational environment for achieving quality in service and implementing the Patient's Charter.

[3] In the 1920s, Elton Mayo conducted experiments at the Hawthorne Plant of the Western Electric Company. When lighting was improved, production went up. The belief was that improved working conditions, ie better lighting, had created a more highly motivated workforce. However when lighting was turned back down, the production rate went *up* again. Reason? The workforce were responding to the interest being taken in them as a result of the research, and *not* to the physical working conditions.

# CHAPTER 2

# The Patient's Charter

## Why is the Patient's Charter relevant to Total Quality?

Total quality is important to every general practice, no matter how advanced or otherwise it is in implementing a local Charter. However, the Patient's Charter embodies at least two important aspects of Total Quality:

- the idea of asking the 'customers' for their suggestions and views
- areas for standard setting.

However, there is much more to a Total Quality Initiative than simply setting standards and expecting staff to achieve and even to exceed them. As discussed in the previous chapter, this book therefore provides guidance on laying the foundation stones of standards of service, both in understanding the practice's current level of achievement, and in harnessing the energy and commitment of the whole team in striving towards common goals.

This chapter does, however, give some background to the Patient's Charter, and the areas it addresses in terms of services for patients.

## The Patient's Charter – History

The Patient's Charter is the development of the Citizen's Charter into the healthcare field. However, it also extends the philosophy of earlier health guidance, including *Promoting Better Health*, and *Working for Patients*.[1]

The Patient's Charter was first implemented in health authorities, hospitals, and community units in 1991, and general practices, as service users, will no doubt be familiar with some of the requirements. Fundholding GPs often refer to the Charter standards in securing the best contracts from provider units for their patients.

National Charter Standards for specific areas have been established. These areas include:

- respect for privacy, dignity, and religious and cultural beliefs
- waiting time for the emergency ambulance service
- waiting time for initial assessment in accident and emergency departments
- waiting time in outpatient clinics
- cancellation of operations
- a named qualified nurse, midwife, or health visitor to be responsible for each patient
- discharge of patients from hospital.

In addition, there is a requirement to set appropriate local standards, including those for:

- waiting times for first outpatient appointment
- waiting times in accident and emergency departments after the need for treatment has been assessed
- waiting times for NHS transport to take the patient home where a medical need for such transport exists
- ways to assist patients and visitors to find their way around hospitals through enquiry points and better signposting

[1] *Promoting Better Health: Management of General Medical Services* HC(FP)(89)20 or HC(89)32.
*Working for Patients*, HMSO, January 1989.

■ name badges for staff who have direct contact with patients and visitors.

Later, three new Charter Rights were added:[2]

1 patients to be given detailed information on local health services, including quality standards and maximum waiting times

2 patients to be guaranteed admission for treatment by a specific date not later than two years from the date when the consultant placed the patient on the waiting list

3 that any complaint about NHS services will be investigated and that the patient will receive a full and prompt written reply from the chief executive or general manager.

The extension of the Patient's Charter into primary care reflects many of the earlier recommendations for the hospital and community services, as well as developing some specific new proposals.

## Development of the Patient's Charter into Primary Care

The extension of the Patient's Charter into primary care is mandatory for FHSAs and required them to meet certain national standards by 1st April 1993. These standards include:

■ helping people to find general practitioners with thom they may register

■ helping them to change doctors easily and quickly

■ transferring notes within two working days when a patient changes doctors.

It also requires FHSAs to co-ordinate and publish information about local medical services. Each FHSA must also define and state its own quality standards.

In addition, FHSAs have a responsibility to facilitate and respond fully and openly to suggestions, comments and complaints. It has been suggested that this should include:

[2] *Implementing the Patient's Charter* HSG(92)4, 17th January 1992.

- acknowledging receipt and notifying the relevant practitioner within two working days

- clearing complaints made under the informal conciliation procedure within one month of receipt

- clearing complaints, to which the service committee procedures apply, within six months.

There is also a requirement to supply both the complainant and the practitioner with monthly progress reports until the issue is finalized.

## Key Points in the Patient's Charter

The charter has three main points of emphasis. These are:

1 it outlines patients' rights in the general medical services

2 it emphasizes patients' responsibilities, both for participating in their own healthcare and treatment, and for not abusing the services provided

3 it provides a 'Users' Guide to Primary Care', bringing together both patients' rights and their responsibilities.

## Charter Areas Directly Affecting General Practitioners

Implementation of the Patient's Charter is currently voluntary for GPs. The guidance recommends the development of local Charters, and suggests that these will be more coherent where they are produced by the primary health care team, rather than by GPs and practice staff alone.

In any event, individual local Charters need to ensure that an overall picture is given of the primary health care services available. They also need to include the Statement of Patients' Rights, and be based on the Users' Guide.

## Development of standards

The Charter suggests that FHSAs may wish to agree area-wide standards in collaboration with the DHAs and Community Units. Under a heading of 'Access', these may include:

- waiting time to see the doctor or nurse, or the patient's doctor of choice, for both urgent and non-urgent conditions
- information about arrangements for contacting the services, for example how quickly they can contact a doctor or nurse by telephone, both during normal surgery and in an emergency
- waiting time for repeat prescriptions
- procedures for dealing with comments, suggestions and complaints, including a named person who will take lead responsibility.

In addition, there is a recommendation that general practitioners may wish to develop additional standards in the following areas:

- physical environment – premises, privacy, facilities for children and disabled people
- procedures and timescales for notifying the results of tests
- the health promotion programmes available
- services for particular client groups or minorities
- the commitment of the primary care team to their own postgraduate training and development, and participation in medical and nursing education generally.

# Conclusion

The Patient's Charter lends itself well to the 'standard-setting' stage of a Total Quality Initiative. When practices are ready to proceed with this stage which is dealt with in Chapter 6, they will find illustrations from the Patient's Charter incorporated into the examples.

The Patient's Charter also has laid down criteria for the monitoring of Charter standards and for seeking consumer views. This is dealt with in Chapter 3.

# Seeking Opinions and Information

# Where Are We Now?
# The 'Health-check' Phase

The purpose of the Health-check Phase is to obtain a picture of your practice as it is now.

There are two main ways of finding out the current position. A combination of both is usually the most effective.

1  The first, very obvious way is to ask the patients! There are several possible methods of undertaking this. However, one of the most cost-effective is by customer survey. Ideally, this should be carried out by an objective third party, but this can be expensive.

   A suitable alternative is to use a questionnaire and to ensure that both it and the scoring methods used are as objective as possible. A sample of a general questionnaire is included in Appendix 1. However, questionnaires may be subject-specific, eg dealing with the appointments system.

2  The second is an internal 'Health-check' or Position Statement. This latter is undertaken by means of:

   ■ an analysis of strengths, weaknesses, opportunities and threats

   ■ semi-structured interviews

   ■ an analysis of systems and procedures

   ■ an analysis of the environment in which care takes place.

These four steps are explained in much more detail in the pages which follow. However, the principal aim of the Health-check Phase is to provide a structured approach to identifying the strengths and weaknesses in the practice, from both the customers' and staff's point of view. It also identifies areas that will benefit from more attention, and perhaps from the setting of specific standards.

# The Customer Survey

## Involving the 'customer'

If part of the concept of Total Quality is constant attention to customer needs then there must be some way of assessing what these needs, and wants, are.

Empowering the patient is as important as empowering the staff, and both are vital in the implementation of Total Quality. In general practice, there are various ways of establishing what the patients' views are, and this Chapter gives some examples of how patient surveys can help. However, many practices also run patient groups where patients are encouraged to give their own view on what they want from the practice. Some practices may even develop these patient groups into full quality circles, where a specific aspect of service provision is looked at from every possible angle with representation from everyone involved in the process, from patients to doctors to nursing staff to clerical staff.

Empowering patients in the health-care arena can be difficult – health is a fettered market, in that patients usually have only limited knowledge of what the product or service can do for them. Patients may not always wish to have services provided in a way which is cost-effective from the provider's point of view. Also, when trying to deliver for the needs of the many it can be particularly difficult to take on board the desires of the few. However most patient groups will understand these constraints provided they feel they genuinely have an opportunity to influence provision.

Perhaps the most basic lesson in seeking patients' opinions is that the practice must be prepared to do something about the results, for the potential consequence of not responding to the majority patient view, once expectations have been raised, is lack of credibility.

This consultation can be conducted using a variety of different consumer survey research techniques. Each has their own advantages and disadvantages, depending on the particular circumstances of each case. These include considerations of:

- degrees of accuracy and reliability required

- levels of depth and detail needed

- number and variety of different aspects covered

- whether new developments are being considered

- the importance of 'confidentiality' of information and opinions expressed (and therefore whether internal staff or external consultants need to be used)

- size, accuracy, and access to the population to be sampled

- whether the subject matter is similar to that covered by any previous research

- if comparisons with other practices or against a 'standard' are necessary

- costs and resources available

- time

- importance of the information to any decisions to be taken.

Seeking patients' opinions is, however, a highly professional task, with many pitfalls for the unwary. Despite this, fear of not carrying out a survey to the required degree of accuracy should not prevent practices from researching their patients' views – on the basis that a picture can be built up gradually over time – and it is important to begin the process, no matter how simple are the initial efforts. As Dr Rod Sheaff has said:

> Start on a modest scale. The practice is still learning, healthcare marketing is still undeveloped and there will be time to add sophistications in future interactions of the marketing cycle.

However, he also warns:

> Arrange at the outset how the results of changes in the service will be monitored – monitoring services is often more time consuming and labour intensive than at first appears.

For those who do decide to carry out a full-scale survey, then it

21

may be appropriate to seek the views of a professional firm from the outset. As the NHS Management Executive's letter entitled *The Patient's Charter: Technical Guidance on Monitoring*[1] states:

> Sampling (including surveys) has many attractions for monitoring some standards. Samples must however be statistically valid. Specialist advice should be obtained locally before starting a survey.

The guidance in the NHS Management Executive's document goes on to outline some of the main considerations in undertaking a survey. For ease of reference, this is included as Appendix 7.

## The Pathfinder consumer survey

As part of the 'Pathfinder Initiative', Hereford and Worcester secured the services of professional Market Research Practitioners (John Ardern Research), who were commissioned to advise on and assist with the most appropriate techniques to aid the development of the Pathfinder Practices.

Two stages of research were completed between September 1991 and January 1992, which answered the questions:

1  *'What makes a good GP/GP practice?'*
(Consisting of a 'qualitative' stage of eight in-depth consumer group discussions, using a primarily non-directive interviewing method).

2  *'How good is your GP/GP practice?'*
(Consisting of the 'quantitative' stage of 418 individual in-home interviews, using a structured questionnaire developed from the results of the initial stage above).

A questionnaire similar to those used in the Pathfinder Initiative is included as Appendix 1. However, again the need for professional advice is stressed, before embarking on an ambitious survey.

[1] *The Patient's Charter: technical guidance on monitoring* dated 30 September 1992, available by writing to DoH store, Health Publications Unit, No 2 Site, Manchester Road, Heywood, Lancashire OL10 2PZ.

Name of practice _____

## ANALYSIS OF STRENGTHS AND WEAKNESSES
Date _____

Under each heading, list the main factors that apply to your practice. Try to list up to six strengths and weaknesses, and three or four opportunities and threats. Do bear in mind the implications of the Patient's Charter.

**S** **Strengths** – ie what does the practice do well? What does your particular section or service excel at?

**W** **Weaknesses** – Be honest! What could be better?

**O** **Opportunities** – What changes in the future are possible in terms of making things better (ie outside changes)?

**T** **Threats** – What outside changes do you see as potentially disadvantageous, eg government changes, FHSA changes, new services being provided by other practices in competition, etc?

**Figure 1:** The SWOT analysis (strengths, weaknesses, opportunities and threats).

| Weaknesses/threats* | Action | Priority<br>High<br>Medium<br>Low | Completion<br>Date for<br>Corrective<br>Action | By whom? |
|---|---|---|---|---|
| | | | | |

* Note: You may not have control over the threats, but identifying them helps to clarify the issues the practice may have to face.
© Hadzor Court. Tel: 0905 794401

**Figure 2:** Action on weaknesses and threats.

# The SWOT Analysis (Strengths, Weaknesses, Opportunities and Threats)

The aim of the SWOT analysis (Figure 1) is to capture a snapshot of the main strengths and weaknesses of the practice and the opportunities and threats which may affect the way in which it works in the future.

This process of information gathering on the position in the practice, *as it is now*, is an early part of both the Total Quality Initiative and of business planning. A SWOT analysis is one of the most useful exercises a practice can undertake to increase self-knowledge.

## Just what is a SWOT analysis?

Most people can identify aspects of the services provided by other organizations, for example hospitals and FHSAs, which they feel either are very good, or perhaps not so good. The aim of a SWOT analysis is to help you identify these for your own practice.

*Strengths* and *weaknesses* are those factors that are internal to the organization – in effect, the aspects which the general practice can control. They ask the question 'What are we good at?' or 'What do we do well?' and conversely 'What do we do less well and could improve upon?' The Patient's Charter should be the framework within which a SWOT analysis is considered.

However, a SWOT analysis does not just look at the service provided. It considers all aspects of the practice and decides the greatest strengths and weaknesses. These may include physical facilities and location as well as staffing aspects.

The second part of the analysis – *opportunities* and *threats* – relates to those aspects outside the practice but which have an effect on the service provided. Obvious examples of the latter include Government changes, length of hospital waiting lists and allocation of finances by the FHSA. However, they may now include more direct competition from other practices and alternative sources of healthcare.

There is a follow-up stage to carrying out a SWOT analysis – to ensure that action is taken on weaknesses and threats where appropriate, so that the process does not become purely a paper exercise! This is called, appropriately enough, 'Action on weaknesses and threats' (*see* Figure 2).

It may not always be possible to correct weaknesses in the short term, especially if they relate to physical factors such as lack of space. However, identifying them at least ensures they are firmly on the agenda for action, and not ignored.

Carrying out a SWOT analysis puts the individual practice into the context of the environment in which it works, so that no outside change (opportunity or threat) is totally unanticipated. This helps the practice to develop contingency plans on a 'What if …?' basis.

Finally, once the strengths and opportunities have been identified, do not forget to give the practice staff a pat on the back! Too often we tend to concentrate on what still needs to be done, rather than on giving praise where it is due.

**KEY POINT – praise the staff for what they already do well!**

### How to carry out the SWOT analysis

This is a part of the health-check phase, which practices can undertake themselves.

A SWOT exercise makes an excellent discussion topic for a practice meeting. However, it is important to have a variety of staff involved, so that no aspects are overlooked. Therefore, practices may find it more useful to include all the staff. To do this, individuals can be asked to complete a SWOT analysis sheet (*see* Figure 1), without conferring at this stage. Occasionally, where there are very sensitive issues, staff may wish to enclose their completed SWOT in an envelope to preserve anonymity.

Following collection of the forms from staff, the results need to be analysed – preferably on computer. All of the points made under each heading (Strengths, Weaknesses, Opportunities and Threats), should be listed, identifying the number of times each is mentioned, to give a priority order.

## Strengths and weaknesses

Strengths may be quite simple to identify, for example:

- happy working environment
- good record of giving speedy appointments with named doctor
- good buildings
- ease of access to building
- well-trained practice manager
- proactive team of GPs
- excellent use of computer
- patients always seen within 20 minutes of appointment time.

Weaknesses may be, for example:

- waiting times in surgery are too long
- inadequate communication from partners to staff
- too many misfiles and missing notes
- staff are unreceptive to change
- telephone answering is too slow
- staff are not fully familiar with the Patient's Charter.

## Opportunities and threats

Opportunities and threats may be perceived differently, depending on whether or not the practice is fundholding.
   Opportunities may include, for example:

- fundholding agreed and accepted
- possibility of developing new services on-site, for example physiotherapy or counselling
- options to increase practice income by taking on a new partner with additional skills
- appointment of a new practice manager with business skills.

Threats may include, for example:

27

- demands on the practice outgrowing the available time

- neighbouring fundholding practices able to offer more services

- constraints on finance for development purposes

- development of new commercial pharmacy (for dispensing practices)

- rescheduling of public transport, making access more difficult.

## Risks in undertaking a SWOT analysis

Although the opportunity given by a SWOT analysis to increase knowledge of the practice is very valuable, there are one or two aspects on which caution is advised.

One danger of undertaking a SWOT analysis is that it puts contentious issues on the agenda and may raise staff dissatisfaction without an obvious answer to problems.

It may require a fundamental change of attitude on the part of some staff, which is difficult, and requires a shift in the very foundations of the atmosphere that pervades the practice. This is known as the 'organizational culture'. Identifying the culture of the practice is a normal part of the 'health-check' phase.

# The Semi-structured Interviews

These interviews ask a number of different people in the practice their views on a predecided range of topics, (hence semi-structured). These interviews need to be carried out by an outsider, ie someone who does not work in the practice on a day-to-day basis. This may be an outside consultant, a Primary Care Facilitator, or even someone from another practice who is experienced in interviewing techniques.

The reasons for using outside help are that:

- this is a highly confidential procedure where staff are encouraged to give frank views to an independent third party

- the questions are designed to quickly bring out any 'trouble-spots', which could be highly sensitive

■ staff are much more likely to feel comfortable in talking to someone who does not have any preconceived views about the practice.

Interviews are time-consuming. It is recommended that a cross-section of staff are included in the interview stage to ensure no key points are missed. In particular, it is essential to interview all the partners, the practice manager, the business manager, (if appropriate), and a representative number of the practice nurses and receptionists, depending on the size of the practice. In addition, if there are practice-based employed or attached staff (for example health visitors, district nurses and physiotherapists), then their view is also invaluable.

## What will we discover from the interviews?

The interviews are designed to give greater depth to the SWOT analysis mentioned earlier. They will quickly reveal how staff feel about the efficiency of their own sphere of work, how others help or hinder it, relationships with both external and internal customers, and how positive staff feel about the atmosphere they work in.

The interviews also pick up the interests and aspirations of staff, and help in the compilation of a skills review and a manpower planning exercise, so that the practice becomes aware of the skills it has available to fulfil present and future practice needs.

The later stages of the interview ask individuals to identify three things they would change if they could. It also seeks their views on what the patients most like and dislike about the practice. Combined, the answers to these questions are a very useful way of confirming the current features of the practice.

As mentioned earlier, the semi-structured interviews should be carried out on your behalf by an objective outsider. However, for interest, an interview form appears as Appendix 2.

# Putting Quality into Specific Aspects of the Practice

# CHAPTER 4

# Quality in Organizational Culture and Management Style

## The Foundations of Total Quality Management

Everyone recognizes a happy environment, or conversely a hostile one, often without being able to explain the differences in tangible terms.

Consider Figure 3 – Organizational Culture – no doubt some of the comments are recognizable in your practice setting! But which characterises your own practice staff (or even some of them) at present?

A positive organizational culture is imperative in introducing a Total Quality Initiative into your practice. This culture is fundamental to the success of securing staff agreement to the practice aims. It therefore provides the whole foundation of a Quality Practice.

During the health-check phase you should receive helpful comments on what your organizational culture is at present. If there are any problem areas, then these will need to be tackled – preferably in advance of, but at least in tandem with, any changes you may wish to introduce.

Good standards of service cannot be grafted on to a base of a resentful staff, ie where staff feel negative about their role and purpose. If this situation exists in a practice then changes are almost impossible to make because staff resistance sabotages progress – this applies even to changes for the better.

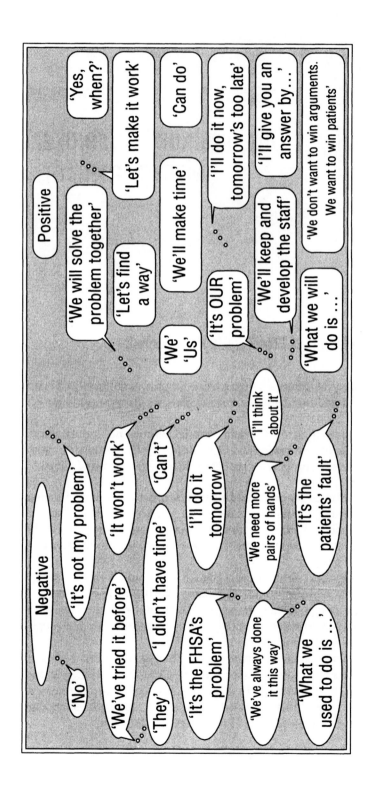

**Figure 3:** Organizational culture

Figure 3 helps to 'diagnose' organizational culture. Similarly, the comments in the checklist that follows will assist in helping to identify your practice's position.

## Checklist

Illustrative examples of a positive organizational culture:

- staff willingness to accept and to suggest change

- enthusiasm of staff for new and better ways of providing the service

- acceptance of personal responsibility by even the lowest grade member of staff in the practice for the quality of his or her work

- low staff turnover (but not unhealthy stagnation)

- constant stream of new ideas from staff

- understanding by staff of the mission statement, the practice values, their own role, and their ability to contribute to the whole.

## How to move towards a positive organizational culture

A positive organizational culture can come only from good management practices. If staff are poorly managed, if their needs are not properly taken into account, or their opinion does not seem to matter, then poor morale and negative responses will result.

> **KEY POINT – the foundation of an effective practice is staff who are treated equitably**

## *Case History 1*

*We were called in to help a practice that had experienced considerable diffi-
culties since it became a third-wave fundholder. The partners believed that
the cause of their difficulties was the way in which one of the staff, who had
been promoted to look after the fund arrangements, was performing. Immediately prior to our visit, they had demoted one member of staff, and made another redundant. They saw it as an 'attitude' problem.*

### *Our approach*

*We started by re-identifying what the issues were. We found that, far from be-
ing clear-cut, the practice's failure to progress its fund satisfactorily was only
one of a number of complex problems. It was, in fact, a symptom rather than
the cause of what was going wrong in the practice.*

*We took a Total Quality approach, first of all looking at the foundation for
achieving results – the organizational culture. We found a thoroughly demoralized workforce. Everyone was aware that the practice had difficulties. The
partners had usurped the practice manager's role, directly giving staff con-
flicting instructions on a day-to-day basis. Everyone was fire-fighting. Staff
who felt they were to 'blame' were very anxious and consequently immobil-
ized with fear of what might happen. Those who were not even involved directly felt they might be next in the firing line.*

*The interference of the partners in a haphazard way had in effect removed
authority from the practice manager, who also felt under-valued. As a result,
the practice manager abdicated responsibility even further, fearing retribu-
tion for the wrong decision.*

*The problem was not one of failure to manage the fund, but failure to man-
age the practice. The partners had given different messages to the staff, there
was no clear and united leadership from the partnership, and staff had no
clear idea of how they were performing. As a result, instead of discussing potential difficulties openly they had hidden what they saw as shortcomings, be-
coming resentful yet trying to please different doctors on an ad hoc basis. The
staff also felt very concerned for the practice manager and fund manager, both
of whom had been demoralized and criticized.*

*We suggested that the partnership immediately agreed a more people-
orientated approach. The 'redundancy' was not proceeded with, and the staff
were reassured that the partners would work together with them to produce
the best result for the practice. The partners agreed to restructure the practice.
They appointed a business manager to look after the whole of the fund and
business plan arrangements, with the previous fund manager and practice
manager accountable to this person. The practice manager was allowed to
manage the practice on a day-to-day basis, and the partners limited themselves to policy and strategy, instead of instructing individual staff! Indi-*

*vidual Performance Review was implemented, and a system of team briefing introduced. Emphasis was put on correcting the systems in terms of managing the fund, instead of blaming the messenger!*

### The Result

*After a few months this was a much happier practice. The partners were working well with the new business manager, and staff morale was much higher: Now that the 'blame' culture was being eradicated, staff were gaining in confidence and coming up with ideas to improve many of the systems in the practice. Both the practice manager and fund manager settled well into the new structure, and no-one was made redundant or demoted. The moral in this story is: first to identify the target, then to take aim, then to fire (do not fire at random hoping to gain a result!). Correct identification of an issue is likely to result in a more accurate solution!*

Two health organization writers, Michael Schofield and Jeffrey Girling, outlined the most vital areas for attention in a pamphlet entitled *Quality and management of health services* [1] These were:

- explicit Mission and Values, communicated with enthusiasm throughout the organization

- empathy with staff and recognition of their value

- equity in interpersonal relationships

- effective decision-making processes based on delegation of responsibility

- open communications.

These views have held good over time. Therefore, if we were to summarize those qualities that distinguish happy and effective general practices, they would be:

- having a philosophy for the practice (Mission and Values), which is understood and shared

- having agreed aims for the practice

- communicating these aims to everyone and securing their acceptance of them

[1] Michael Schofield and Jeffrey Girling, (1989) *Quality and management of health services*, Institute of Health Services Management, London.

■ putting as much effort into understanding, encouraging and recognizing the value of staff as of the end customer, ie the patient.

The list at the end of the chapter outlines some important areas of practice management where a practice can take action to encourage a positive organizational culture. Action taken in these areas is always worth-while because it has a cumulative effect. For example, Individual Performance Review (IPR), if properly implemented, is likely to have an extremely beneficial impact. It is recommended as one of the most important contributory factors to improving the underlying morale of the practice[2]. It does, however, need careful implementation. If it is introduced to the staff in the wrong way, then more harm than good can be done. For this reason, you are recommended to seek appropriate advice. However, for interest, the relevant paperwork has been included as Appendix 3.

Individual performance review is a structured method of agreeing objectives with each member of staff. Objectives should be in line with the aims of the practice business plan. Each individual is expected to achieve their objectives within an agreed timescale. Objectives are reviewed, performance evaluated, and new objectives agreed at a major review each year. Interim reviews are carried out, usually at six-monthly intervals. The personal development needs of individuals are also addressed. Undertaken correctly, after appropriate training, IPR is one of the most effective methods any organization can use of ensuring cohesion between overall aims, group targets and individual objectives.

**KEY POINT – don't sweep 'attitude' problems under the carpet – they *can* be solved!**

---

[2] By focusing on results – individual and team performance, as well as what is most beneficial for the practice – no-go areas or 'sacred cows' can be tackled.

Appendix 4 is an Action Sheet to help you consider these aspects the action needed to implement them, and a timetable for achieving results.

## Encouraging a positive organizational culture

■ an effective recruitment and induction system

■ individual Performance Review (IPR) in place

■ as part of the Individual Performance Review, jointly agreed Personal Action Plan and Development Programme in place for each member of staff

■ team briefing *in situ*, ie a system for ensuring that the dissemination of information is effective and timely, to prevent rumour and inaccurate communication

■ a Mission and Values Statement, agreed by partners and staff, written down and disseminated

■ an open style of management. This is one based on maximum delegation, which actively encourages staff to take calculated risks and try out new ideas. With such a style there are no 'no-go' areas and no sanction for making mistakes. Decision-making is delegated to the lowest possible level. It is excellent as a contributory factor to good staff development.

# CHAPTER 5

# The Physical Environment

## Quality in the Physical Surroundings in which Patients are Received

It is difficult in everyday practice life to stay aware of the surroundings in which one works. Particular constraints may cause repeated difficulties which, because of familiarity with the situation, may no longer be noticed by staff.

This brief chapter has been included, therefore, to act as a checklist to enable staff to reassess the good and less than good points about the environment in which they work, and where patients are received and advised.

The aim of this section is not to recommend wholesale rebuilding or redevelopment of the practice premises. This may be desirable, but it should form part of an overall Business Plan, and not be treated as an isolated event.

Instead, the objective here is to identify key aspects of the environment to establish what can be improved upon within the existing facilities. Special note should be taken of the Patient's Charter references to the physical environment, which include privacy, access for disabled and facilities for children.

Sometimes, progress is difficult to make because the issue seems to be one of space or layout. However, an important factor is to think laterally – do not simply consider past problems and assume there is no solution. Sometimes it is necessary to stand back from the problem and brainstorm all possible options.

## Case History 2

*A five-partner practice was in health centre premises. Although the practice list had grown, no extra space had been allocated by the Health Authority, despite repeated requests. As a result, doctors and other professionals were sharing surgery space, the practice manager was situated in the reception area, and the practice nurses, who shared a treatment room and had no office, used one desk between them – also in the reception area. The situation reached crisis point when the practice decided to become fourth-wave fundholders. There was absolutely nowhere to provide a fund office or to locate the necessary additional computers.*

### Our approach

*The practice was advised to take a much wider view of the problem, and assess, by observation, what available space there appeared to be in the health centre as a whole. Over a period of weeks, Health Authority use of the building was monitored, and a picture built up of where there appeared to be under-used accommodation. In particular, a large, enclosed pram shelter at the main entrance was a 'white-elephant' never used by visitors to the centre.*

*Armed with factual information, the practice approached the Health Authority again, and made its case for transfer of the pram shelter to the practice. At the same time, an application was made to the FHSA for the funding to convert the pram shelter to office accommodation.*

*Both authorities agreed. In particular, the Health Authority was keen to co-operate with the practice, who as a potential new purchaser from the provider unit in question (the Community Trust), now had far more negotiating power.*

### The result

*The pram shelter was converted into two offices – one for fundholding and one for the practice manager. Secretarial staff who had previously occupied a shared office in the main surgery area also moved to the newly acquired building, freeing up space for the nursing staff.*

### The moral

*Do not assume that because someone has said 'No' in the past, the situation*

*will remain the same in the future. Fundholding has changed general prac-*
*tices' negotiating power.*

On a more general note, it is important to use the talents you have in the practice. Almost certainly, there will be someone who is good at co-ordinating colours and arranging furnishings to the best advantage. Very often, huge differences in atmosphere can be made by very minor changes in colour (curtains, seat cushions, even lampshades and pictures), to produce a co-ordinated effect.

Over-harsh lighting is also one of the most common mistakes in producing an uncomfortable, clinical feel in surgeries.

Minor details can also greatly improve the atmosphere. One of the original Pathfinder Practices made it someone's responsibility every week to put a bowl of fresh flowers on the reception desk. Paper clutter was never noticed as patients commented on how attractive the flowers were! Pleasant details like these create a focal point in key areas, and detract from less desirable aspects.

Appendix 5 is a check-list for assessing your practice premises. It addresses the visitor's impression of the surgery in terms of the Patient's Charter – attractiveness, convenience, and comfort, together with confidentiality.

**KEY POINT – identify the artistic skills of your staff and ask them to look at the surgery through new eyes!**

# CHAPTER 6

# Quality in Systems and Procedures

## General Comments

### Procedures and systems

Total Quality requires that every procedure and process in practice is audited to assess what *could* go wrong, and take preventive action – in other words, it irons out potential hiccoughs in the system – prevention, not cure. The perfected process is then written up as a practice protocol.

Practices will need to detail the tasks they carry out in each area. In the widest sense these can include aspects such as the processes involved in:

- doctors' visits
- referral and follow-up arrangements
- dealing with investigation results
- telephone answering
- appointment systems
- repeat prescriptions
- managing incoming and outgoing post
- organizing staff rotas and on-call cover

- filing

- handling suggestions and complaints

- ordering of goods and services

- dealing with FHSA returns and contract paperwork.

The practice will be able to identify many other areas.

When designing a new procedure the thought process is similar to a route march – one wishes to travel from A to B by the easiest route, avoiding pitfalls. Yet all too frequently when implementing a new system into the daily routine of practice life, good ideas fail to produce results, usually because of lack of detail and planning.

This section, therefore, aims to give examples of some of those systems and procedures in practice life that appear to create the most difficulties.

First of all, however, three general aspects must be addressed if it is decided to review and possibly to change any of the existing systems.

## Step 1 – Define the Procedure

- Outline the aim of the procedure to be implemented, for example the aim may be 'to increase the efficiency of the present postal system within the practice'.

- Outline the *current* process.

- Outline the proposed process, including a list of the known advantages for the proposed new system.

- Compare with the disadvantages of the present system – and assess the need for change!

## Step 2 –Assess the Effects on Staff

The 'people' issues are vital to making successful changes. Questions to be asked include the following.

- What is the current staffing structure?

- Who will be most affected by the change? Will the change alter any job descriptions?

- What extra training will be needed and who will deal with the training aspects of the new system?

- Who will monitor the system and for how long should the new procedure be monitored?

- Will staff have to be given any extra hours for training and/or for handling the new system?

- Will the new system be cost effective in man-hours?

- How effective are the existing *communication systems* in the practice? What is the state of staff morale? Can they cope with the proposed changes, or do we need to work on attitudes first?

## Step 3 – Consider the broader implications for general aspects of practice management

- Outline the strengths and weakness of the practice's organizational skills – be aware of any pitfalls.

- Could existing technology, eg computers or fax, aid the new proposals? Will new software be required? Will this be cost-effective?

- Finance! Will the new procedure increase income – either long or short term? What are the *cost benefits* of the proposal?

- Will the new system aid in audit?

- Will extra space have to be created?

- In conclusion: are there adequate resources to fully implement and support the new system?

**KEY POINT – be sure any changes are discussed fully with staff before attempting implementation**

Generally, when planning a new system, a very positive approach must be adopted and great care taken to *communicate* at all times.

Always bear in mind that change can appear very threatening, but a new idea or procedure that is well planned and shows clear advantages to the practice, will stir the interest and enthusiasm of the practice team.

# Examples of aspects to consider with specific systems

## Appointments

A very significant area of debate in surgery life is the practice appointment system! Appointment control affects partners, staff, and patients alike – usually causing some frustration. Breakdowns of the system cause major problems for *all* parties, and frequently there is little management control.

Recognition of what each party expects from an appointment system must be examined carefully, agreements reached and monitored, and results acted upon. The Patient's Charter is an important consideration in deciding the type of appointments system the practice should be offering.

Questionnaires can be given to patients to explore their views, but is it also important to examine feelings within the practice itself, and for the views of all parties to be examined carefully and sympathetically.

Practices are now offering a vast range of services to their patients, and there is a wealth of variety amongst the Health Promotion Clinics. However, patients still need to be seen for routine appointments, acute/urgent cases have to be dealt with promptly, and non-GMS services have to be catered for – all within a normal working day!

Good management control is therefore essential, and practices should take the opportunity to explore their own feelings in conjunction with those of their patients.

The daily diary sheet that has been so popular in practice life for the past decade or so may also have to be reviewed. The Hadzor consultants, bearing this in mind, developed a planning system to help practices accommodate all the weekly activities on one A3 sheet, which is a superb 'tool' for the accurate management of practice activities. However, we suggest you start by seeking views on your existing systems. Appendix 6A 'The Appointments

Questionnaire (Partners)' and Appendix 6B 'Patients' Views on Appointments' will help you to do this.

**KEY POINT – you may need to stand back and reassess the whole of your appointment system's effectiveness**

## Contract paperwork

The advent of the 1990 contract created a great deal of paperwork for the practice to handle in order to claim payments for the practice activities. It is essential, therefore to create – either by computer or manually – an efficient system to ensure:

■ that correct payments for items of service and target payments, etc. are received

■ that the paperwork is dealt with swiftly and effectively

■ that the practice maintains control of the paperwork.

### Important New Issues in the Contract Paperwork

*Overall Management of Claims*

■ Ensure, after fully completing claims forms – including doctor's signature and practice stamp – that the office management system guarantees that each claim is recorded before being sent to the FHSA.

■ Maximize income by ensuring claims are sent promptly during the claiming quarter.

■ Where a computing medical business system is used, inform the FHSA. Even if a link is not yet possible, there may be future advantages with movements towards a paperless environment.

49

**Figure 4:** Note culling.

## Discard    LETTERS

- ☐ Hospital discharge slips – if **summaries** available
- ☐ Serial letters re same operation (eg hernia repair)…but
  *keep* all histology
  *keep* one significant letter
- ☐ Follow-up letters on chronic illness with **no new abnormalities**
- ☐ Postnatal discharge letter unless **abnormal**. *Record normal delivery on summary card, eg 'normal deliv. male infant at 38/40'*
- ☐ All maternity correspondence more than five years old, including GPs' referral letters
- ☐ Postnatal discharge letters – record Agpar score, Guthrie test and arc test at top of FP7/8

## Discard    CARDS

- ☐ All blank cards
- ☐ Duplicate immunization cards
- ☐ Other immunization cards **after** transferring information to main FP7A/9A (eg BCG, measles, etc.)
  **LEAVE ANTENATAL RECORD CARDS *IN SITU***

## Discard    X-RAYS

- ☐ Negative chest X-rays – **but always keep the most recent**
  **NEVER DISCARD ANY X-RAY AFTER TRAUMA**

## Discard    RESULTS

- ☐ Old pregnancy tests
- ☐ Old prothrombin test results
- ☐ Urine cultures more than one year old
- ☐ Normal cervical smear results – **where recorded onto either manual or computer records**
  *keep **all abnormal** smear results*
- ☐ HVS more than one year old
- ☐ Normal haematology more than one year old
- ☐ Normal biochemistry more than one year old
  **KEEP ALL MICROBIOLOGY RESULTS**

- Photocopy and identify each claim sent to the FHSA – keep each category of claim under separate cover and per quarter.

- Take control of paperwork – file correctly!

*Training of Staff*

- Train every member within the office team to complete forms correctly.

- Produce and agree protocols with the partners on management of systems, eg recording of minor surgeries.

- Prepare 'mock' samples of each claim form to enter into the Protocol Pack.

- Ensure that office staff are taking responsibility for forms and their correct completion.

## Patients' case notes

As well as the increase in contract paperwork, there is, of course, a huge volume of paperwork contained within the patients' notes.

Culling or pruning notes will reduce bulk inside the medical records envelopes, where space is at a premium. Culling has become a matter of necessity in many practices.

The guide given below is for use as a framework only – each practice should discuss fully its own personal culling procedure, as the partners may vary in what they believe should be discarded. In particular, it is of course important to fulfil legal requirements on retention of notes.

If you are still using Lloyd George envelopes, it would be well worth considering the advantage of changing to A4 in the future. Although this takes up more space in terms of height, the bulk is less. All hospitals, FHSAs and other organizations have now standardized on A4, and it does reduce the amount of trimming and folding required to make letters fit the Lloyd George envelopes! Figure 4 gives a suggested outline of what may be culled from the notes.

## Post

The post is, of course, an assortment of paperwork entering the surgery, and is received daily, so effective systems are crucial for

**Figure 5:** Post procedures check-list

The aim is to devise a system that ensures swift action on incoming mail. It can also act as a guide to new staff who deal with the post.

Tick when systems are in place:

☐ IN/OUT trays for each partner and practice manager

☐ Staff trained in postal procedures

☐ 'Sifting' agreed and in place

☐ Letters/reports 'banded' together

☐ Insurance reports held in separate file

☐ PMA requests inserted into patients' notes

☐ Notes placed in doctors' 'IN' tray

☐ Magazines 'banded' together

☐ Advertising literature 'banded' together

☐ Prescriptions – to office staff for actioning

☐ FHSA/RHA correspondence etc. to practice manager

Note 1    Remove all path results (cervical smears/X-rays) after doctor has made comments. Enter these into RESULTS BOOK or onto COMPUTER for easy access to this information should a patient telephone for a result, eg cholesterol result required.

Note 2    For fundholding purposes a results book is useful for auditing practice pathology and X-ray activity.

staying on top of it! Figure 5 shows a brief checklist for sifting incoming mail.

The post can be divided into various categories – patient information (letters and results), medical literature, advertising mail, and FHSA claims paperwork.

Management control must ensure that the post is dealt with promptly, circulated to the correct partner, action taken where appropriate, and filed as quickly as possible. It may be useful to consider using a 'stamp' process to speed incoming mail through the practice, as illustrated in Figure 6. Using this simple stamp process, the partner can control the mail. If the partner uses a single stroke to action the stamp (* in Figure 6), once the matter has been accomplished the 'action' is then crossed (** in Figure 6). As soon as all the directions from the partner have been actioned the letter/result can be filed.

All post should be stamped with the date of receipt.

All staff should be familiar with the types of correspondence and know how to act upon the partners' instructions.

---

**Figure 6:** The 'stamp' process

|  | |  |
|---|---|---|
| File | | * File in patient's notes |
| Doctor | | Enter name of partner |
| For computer | | Work to enter on computer |
| Tel Pt. normal | | Result information |
| Doctor to speak | | ** Dr wishes to speak to patient |
| To make appt. | | Patient to book appointment |
| Notes please | | Notes to partner |
| Pick up prcptn. | | Collect prescription |
| Questionnaire | | Audit/fundholding purposes |
| PN/MW/etc | | For other member of team |
| | | Other free comment |

**Figure 7:** Repeat prescribing

Tick when actioned

## Staff Requirements:

☐ Train staff in repeat prescribing practice, bearing in mind the Patient's Charter.

☐ If the practice permits repeat prescription request by telephone, train members of office team to input repeat prescriptions directly onto the computer.

☐ Try to install a dedicated line for repeat prescribing.

☐ If a manual system is in place for scripts ensure each prescription is double-checked before handing to doctor for signature.

☐ Train staff in computer prescription techniques as early as possible.

## Management Requirements:

☐ Agree the relevant standards and targets for repeat prescribing.

☐ Have a protocol for repeat prescribing, and ensure all staff know and understand it.

☐ Monitor 'high cost' drugs for budget-control, especially in fundholding.

☐ Implement a practice formulary.

☐ Review PACT information – monitor prescribing habits.

## Patients' Responsibilities:

☐ Encourage patients to post their repeat prescription requests one week before their medication runs out.

☐ Do not encourage 'last minute' ordering.

☐ When the patient policy is for ALL repeats to be posted, and/or over the counter, encourage patients to use the computerized repeat order slip.

☐ Encourage patients (where telephone requests are permitted) to telephone only in the early afternoons, so as not to block practice telephone lines during busy practice activity times.

KEY POINT – good
paperwork management
buys the practice more of
that vital commodity – time!

## Prescriptions

It is vital for the partnership to agree a protocol on repeat prescribing. New patients should be made aware of the repeat prescribing policy, and existing patients should be expected to comply with practice policy in all normal circumstances. There are mixed views about how quickly repeat prescriptions should be available for collection. Some of the Pathfinder practices successfully maintained a 24-hour standard. Another achieved a 48-hour standard, but was aiming for a 24-hour target[1]. Yet a third managed a 48-hour target with 100 per cent success, and saw no necessity to set a new target, believing that patients found 48 hours totally acceptable.

The main point here is to ensure you have a standard and target that is acceptable to the patients, bearing in mind the Patient's Charter, and one that invariably is attained. Patient education (patients' responsibilities) is a key factor in ensuring that the system works effectively.

In order to achieve the standard – at whatever level it is agreed – effective systems are crucial. Figure 7 provides a check-list to help practices implement effective systems.

KEY POINT – use the
Patient's Charter politely to
remind patients how they
can help you to help them

[1] For a description of standards and targets, *see* page 67.

## Case History 3

*A seven-partner practice in a country town constantly mentioned the irritations of starting surgery without the notes – even for patients who had booked appointments. Instead, practice staff were offering blank case sheets, to be entered into the notes when these turned up. This was affecting relationships in the practice – the doctors were embarrassed if they could not remember why the patient had last consulted. In addition, there was a feeling, although not openly stated, that staff varied in their ability both to produce the correct notes on time, and file them in the correct place.*

*By the time we were asked to advise, relationships had deteriorated to the stage where staff felt criticized and reluctant to put themselves out to find notes, feeling that others did not pull their weight.*

*The Senior Receptionist in the practice also felt criticized, and complained that the staff were 'doing their best'.*

### Solution

*We advised the practice to take a Total Quality approach – in other words, to identify the potential contributory factors to the situation and to eradicate potential problems in a systematic way. Total Quality looks at the whole process and everyone takes responsibility to reach agreed standards – it does not look for people to blame when things go wrong.*

*The approach we advised brought together several aspects of organizational culture, as well as performance standards.*

### Example – Misfiles

*As a first stage, the total problem should be correctly identified by asking some specific questions. Therefore, a brief survey to establish the extent of the problem, the number of missing notes/misfiles on specific dates, and a note of all factors contributing to the problem is the first step.*

*These types of problems are often related to leadership. Therefore the organization and level of proactive management amongst the receptionists should be examined. Questions to ask are:*

- *Who is responsible for leading the receptionists on a day-to-day basis?*

- *Is this working, or are there strong personalities diluting the leadership role?*

- *Is the problem being dealt with actively enough, or is it seen as an unavoidable nuisance?*

- *Are the misfiles known to be more of a problem with some staff than with others?*

- *Who is taking responsibility on a day-to-day basis for analysing why the problem has occurred?*

- *Has an audit trail been undertaken to establish the weak points in the process, and revamp the procedures, which all staff should adhere to?*

- *Who are the other players in the field who contribute to missing notes? What action should be taken by them to resolve the situation?*

As a general rule, the only way to solve varying standards is to make sure that each indivdual has 'ownership' of the standard of work they achieve.

A protocol for dealing with notes – who should do what, by when, by what process in various circumstances – needs to be developed and agreed with staff.

At this point, the reception team will agree their own quality standard. For example,

'98 per cent of files will be returned to their correct place within 24 hours of being pulled', The minimum standard for misfiles will be 5 per cent per month', and 'The target for misfiles will be 2 per cent per month by the end of July 1994'.

The staff involved (receptionists) should then be asked to solve the problem of how individual staff are identified (specific drawers for specific doctors, etc). The receptionists will have much more ownership of the problem if they are given the responsibility of solving it themselves, using the approach we have outlined. Colour-coding of notes (eg all 'A's tagged red, 'B's purple, 'C's blue, etc) is simple and effective both in alerting staff to file correctly and in highlighting misfiles.

As a further stage, it must be agreed who will take responsibility for monitoring and evaluating the success of the filing system, ie someone to record missing notes and misfiles with as much information as possible as to the cause. These standards should be reviewed at the end of each target period.

The final stage is to ensure that the agreed standard is linked with IPR so that each individual receptionist is aware of their own standard compared to that of the group. Targets for improvement should be agreed with individuals, as well as with the group.

## The result

Identifying the areas where mistakes could occur raised everyone's awareness of the importance of carefully following agreed procedures. There was, in fact, one receptionist who consistently misfiled – and another who felt too pressurized to break off what she was doing to seek out missing notes. Yet another issue that emerged was that it was felt that the part-time morning staff were leaving difficult misfiles for the afternoon staff to sort out. This created undue

**57**

*pressure on the afternoon staff, who still had to find the notes, but in a shorter period of time!*

*The process also highlighted the need for staff to recognize the internal customer concept – the process that requires them to recognize each other's needs in producing a good service for the end customer – in this case the patient. The doctors were entitled to a good service from the receptionists, as they were their internal customers.*

*At the end of the day, tightening up on the misfiles, by allocating drawers to individual receptionists to look after (possible in large practices) and by monitoring the rate of misfiles in each, it was possible to link up the results with the performance standards in the IPR. In summary, therefore, team objectives in reception set the agreed standard for misfiles, while individuals became aware of their own performance in relation to that of the team. Ownership of standards helps them to be achieved!*

### The moral

*Don't just complain about misfiles. Analyse the whole filing process and staff attitudes to identify where problems may occur.*

## Office protocol pack

A full office protocol pack containing guides for the sort of non-medical procedures discussed in this chapter should be produced to ensure standardization within the practice. Not only does this benefit existing staff by giving firm and direct guidance, but it also helps to familiarize new staff with the practice requirements.

Protocol packs also supply useful information to partners, practice nurses and trainee doctors in the surgery. A well-produced protocol pack can help in the dissemination and monitoring of standards. The production of the pack can be undertaken by members of the ancillary team, and can be a rewarding team-building exercise for those who contribute.

A further use for the protocol pack is that it serves as a useful training aid within the practice. It should be informative, clear, and with some lighter moments!

The pack should be a guide – always left accessible to existing members of staff who may wish to query an aspect of their work, as well as an insight into surgery activities by a new member of staff. It should make easy reading as well as being informative.

A well-written office protocol pack is a useful tool for the practice manager to study periodically and implement change where necessary.

**Figure 8:** Sample content of a protocol pack

The protocol pack should include: (tick when achieved)

- [ ] A warm welcome to the surgery from all partners.

- [ ] A brief background of the practice (with photos if possible).

- [ ] Profiles of the partners and staff.

- [ ] A brief outline of The Patient's Charter, together with the practice's agreed standards.

- [ ] Protocol for reception of patients, visits and messages.

- [ ] Protocols for registration of new patients – including new patient health checks.

- [ ] Flow charts to demonstrate the systems employed, eg from the registration of a new patient to receiving the patient's notes from the FHSA.

- [ ] Protocols for claims procedures – to include 'mock' samples of ALL claim forms. Emphasis must be placed upon correctly completing claim forms.

- [ ] Protocol on editing and culling notes.

- [ ] Protocol on temporary residents.

- [ ] Protocol on repeat prescriptions.

- [ ] Protocol on post system.

- [ ] Protocol on filing system.

- [ ] Guide to medical terminology and abbreviations used within the practice.

- [ ] Guidance upon the various clinics offered within the practice.

- [ ] Guidance on the practice's non-GMS work.

- [ ] Brief introduction to the computer system.

- [ ] Protocol for travel advice.

- [ ] Guidance on Individual Performance Review (IPR).

- [ ] A summary of the Business Plan of the practice.

- [ ] And some lighter moments, such as social events, outings undertaken by the practice – including a copy of the practice staff magazine (if produced), etc.

The pack is best prepared in a format that can be added to easily or adjusted – the plastic punched wallet-type folders are ideal. It should be simple, readable, and step-by-step, in a format that new recruits can digest on their own.

Although it will take a little while to produce, it will state the standards expected from the office team and guidelines to ensure the efficient running of the practice. Figure 8 gives a description of what should be included in a protocol pack.

**KEY POINT** – the Protocol
Pack can make
communication within the
team more effective

# Measuring Quality in Specific Aspects of the Practice

# CHAPTER 7

# Setting Standards and Targets

The previous sections will have identified for you the areas that you most wish to address in your own practice. Once you have identified some of the potential problem areas it is important to decide how to ensure that standards are implemented and improvements are maintained, in line with the Patient's Charter.

The aim of this section is to help practices to consider how standards may be set and monitored. Some standards may be readily measurable, such as waiting times, whilst others may be more intangible.

As mentioned in the early sections of this book, it is accepted that ultimate outcomes are very difficult to measure in terms of health. The monitoring role of FHSAs and the development of medical audit and clinical protocols is geared towards outcome measures.

However, there are also what are known as 'process' standards. What this means, in effect, is that if we can improve the process of how the patient receives health care, eg by ensuring that the patient's experience of visiting the surgery is as comfortable and effective as possible, then we will have taken all possible steps to contribute to a favourable overall outcome for the patient.

To make this process easier to implement, we have provided examples of measures that the Pathfinder practices found to be appropriate for them. Yours may be similar. You will certainly wish to take account of the Patient's Charter initiatives, and we have given examples of how these could be applied to standard setting.

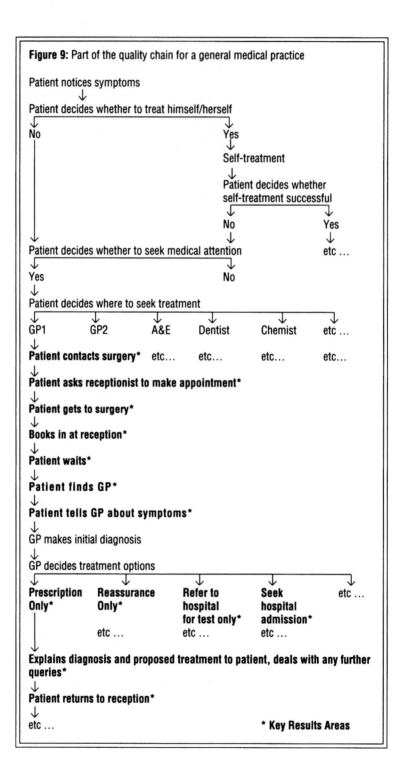

**Figure 9:** Part of the quality chain for a general medical practice

Patient notices symptoms
↓
Patient decides whether to treat himself/herself

No                                                        Yes
                                                           ↓
                                                        Self-treatment
                                                           ↓
                                                        Patient decides whether
                                                        self-treatment successful
                                                           ↓                    ↓
                                                          No                   Yes
                                                           ↓                    ↓
Patient decides whether to seek medical attention                            etc ...
↓                                    ↓
Yes                                  No
↓
Patient decides where to seek treatment

GP1         GP2         A&E         Dentist        Chemist        etc ...
↓
**Patient contacts surgery***    etc...      etc...        etc...         etc...
↓
**Patient asks receptionist to make appointment***
↓
**Patient gets to surgery***
↓
**Books in at reception***
↓
**Patient waits***
↓
**Patient finds GP***
↓
**Patient tells GP about symptoms***
↓
GP makes initial diagnosis
↓
GP decides treatment options

↓                    ↓                    ↓                    ↓                    ↓
**Prescription**    **Reassurance**    **Refer to**        **Seek**            etc ...
**Only***           **Only***          **hospital**        **hospital**
                                       **for test only***  **admission***
                    etc ...            etc ...             etc ...
↓
**Explains diagnosis and proposed treatment to patient, deals with any further queries***
↓
**Patient returns to reception***
↓
etc ...                                        * Key Results Areas

One useful way of proceeding is to consider a patient's flow-chart (Figure 9). This looks at the patient from the time he or she first decides to consult on a problem, to the final outcome. By studying the flow-chart, it is possible to identify interfaces between the practice staff and the patient, which are important communication points. These communication points lend themselves well to standard setting.

Initially, practices are likely to find it difficult to set standards in appropriate and measurable terms, but it does become easier with practice.

# The Approach to Setting Standards

The aim of this section is to produce essential standards of service in the most important areas. The approach has three steps.

1 Identifying 'key result' areas.

2 Specifying minimum standards in each key result area.

3 Agreeing programme targets for standards above the minimum.

## Identifying key result areas

Key Result Areas are the aspects of the practice by which 'customers' judge it, and which are most important in helping it to achieve its aims. If the practice does not recognize its key result areas, it will jeopardize the service it is trying to achieve (Figure 10).

For example, the Key Result Areas of a reception service, are to receive patients appropriately and to ensure the patient's comfort during their transactions with the staff, at the same time ensuring that the service they provide is effective. Therefore, Key Result Areas cover both what is done, and how it is done.

As mentioned above, it is easier to identify those areas at which the patient receives a service, and agree minimum standards and targets in those areas. However, other illustrative Key Result Areas for the practice as a whole, and which are implicit in the Patient's Charter, include:

**65**

**Figure 10:** Identifying Key Result Areas

## Sample exercise

This is a sample exercise, designed to provide the opportunity for you to identify areas which you feel are *crucial* to the outcome of *one* part of the service your practice provides, eg Patient Reception.

You may wish to undertake this exercise with the practice team, and ultimately to extend it to other practice areas. In any event, consider the guidance available in the Patient's Charter before deciding key result areas.

Example: What are the most important, or *Key* Result Areas in Patient Reception?

Write out your initial thoughts on six Key Result Areas below:

| | KEY RESULT AREAS |
|---|---|
| 1 | |
| 2 | |
| 3 | |
| 4 | |
| 5 | |
| 6 | |

CHECK

Do your first thoughts on Key Result Areas capture the most important elements of the service? Do they capture the main elements of the Patient's Charter? Put another way, would you be content for this service to be judged on the basis of performance in these areas? If you provided a poor service in these areas, what would be the result in terms of patients' views of the practice (or FHSA views for example)?

■ patients' overall satisfaction with service – including sound procedures for dealing with comments, suggestions and complaints

■ access to services – length of waiting time for appointments, offer of appointment with named doctor and practice nurse, for both urgent and non-urgent requests

■ ease of communication with the surgery, eg contacting providers by telephone, both during normal opening hours and in an emergency

■ a quality surgery environment, eg facilities for parents and children, and for the disabled. Standard of waiting and consulting facilities

■ a quality atmosphere, ie the more 'intangible' environment. How genuinely happy and well-motivated are the staff? Are there any 'issues' between staff which affect morale?

■ preservation of patients' dignity and privacy

■ procedures for notifying test results and for obtaining repeat prescriptions

■ facilities for particular client groups and/or minorities.

## Specifying minimum standards

Standards of performance are needed for each Key Result Area (Figure 11). They should describe a minimum level of performance which it is reasonable to assume is attainable. The Patient's Charter defines a standard as, 'A level of service which the patient can expect to be delivered other than in exceptional cases.'

A miniumum standard for a reception desk, where, for example, staff have identified 'prompt telephone answering' as a Key Result Area in patient satisfaction, might be that:

■ 90 per cent of telephone calls are answered by the fourth ring.

However, standards must be achievable! Therefore the standard:

■ does not assume that 100 per cent of telephone calls can be answered within four rings. There are always going to be occasions when other events behind the reception desk prevent perfection

**Figure 11:** Setting standards from Key Result Areas

Think about possible standards for each of your Key Result Areas. Write in your thoughts below, again taking into account the Patient's Charter.

| KEY RESULT AREA (Repeat those outlined in Figure 10) | POSSIBLE STANDARD (How will you measure results?) |
|---|---|
| 1. | |
| 2. | |
| 3. | |
| 4. | |
| 5. | |
| 6. | |

CHECK: DO YOUR STANDARDS

1. Indicate how well you are doing in the Key Result Areas?
2. Allow measurement of performance?

■ refers to the general performance of the reception staff over a period of time, not what should happen to each telephone call on every occasion

■ it is a standard which any competent practice can achieve. It does not require exceptional ability!

KEY POINT – standard levels of service should be attainable other than in *exceptional cases*

Some other examples of possible areas for standard setting, which are taken directly from the Patient's Charter, are given in Figure 12.

KEY POINT – keep measures simple and brief and concentrate on the most important aspects

QUALITY

**Figure 13:** Targets for improvement

With your practice team, think about possible improvements in
standards, which can be achieved in the next twelve months within the
areas you have already identified. When there is general agreement,
complete a summary of the results of this and the previous two
exercises as indicated below, again ensuring that the Patient's Charter
has been fully considered.

| Key practice areas for improvement | Minimum standards | Targets | Action required by whom? By when? | Completion date |
|---|---|---|---|---|
| | | | | |

CHECK

1. Are the targets achievable?
2. Are they sufficiently challenging?
3. How will you check performance?
4. Do they implement and complement the Patient's Charter

**Figure 12:** Key results and standards

| KEY RESULT AREA | POSSIBLE AREAS FOR STANDARD SETTING |
|---|---|
| Patient satisfaction with service | a) Clear system for handling suggestions, comments and complaints.<br>b) Acceptable percentage/level of complaints per year (eg less than 1% of patients complain). |
| Good customer/patient relations with emphasis on obtaining consumer input and feedback | a) Acceptable percentage of positive comments (through consumer surveys). Corrective action taken where necessary. |
| Access to services | a) Percentage of patients offered an appointment within a set time with a named doctor (eg 99% of patients offered an appointment within 24 hours with named doctor). |
| Length of waiting time in the surgery | a) Percentage of patients seen within $X$ minutes of their appointment time (eg 99% seen within 20 minutes). |
| A quality surgery environment | a) Difficult to put in hard measures, so include a check list (*see* appendix 4):<br>*Physical environment, eg:*<br>• comfortable seating in appropriate layout<br>• co-ordinated colour scheme/ furnishings<br>• reading material to suit patients which is up-to-date (whose role to check?)<br>• privacy<br>• facilities for children/special client groups/minority groups |
| Repeat prescriptions | a) $X$% ready and signed within $X$ (eg 95% ready and signed withing 24 hours). |
| Together with the 'intangible' environment or *how* patients are received | a) For example: patients are always greeted on arrival, even if receptionist has to break off from other tasks.<br>b) Explanations given if patients are kept waiting beyond appointment time. |

There are many more possible Quality Standards – other Key Result Areas could include, for example, developing models of good practice for:
■ Communications within the extended Primary Health Care Team;
■ Relationships with outside agencies, eg FHSAs, hospitals, Social Services Departments – especially with regard to transfer of information.

## Agreeing targets (improvements on current standards)

Many standards are capable of being improved upon. The improvements can be realized by better organization in many instances and are not dependent on major changes (Figure 13).

Generally speaking, a target is an agreed level of performance *above the minimum*: an example from an appointments system is given in Figure 14.

---

Figure 14: Key results, standards and targets

| KEY RESULT AREA | STANDARD | TARGET |
|---|---|---|
| Patients requiring an appointment | X% given an appointment within 24 hours of initial request with named doctor | X + 10% given an appointment within 24 hours of initial request with named doctor |

---

However, a target may also be the level of service that is being aimed for, but which cannot be reached immediately. The Patient's Charter (HSG (92) 36) states that, 'Targets can also be used as staging posts on the way to the full achievement of a standard.'

KEY POINT – today's targets may become tomorrow's standards – constant improvement is the theme

## *Case History 4*

*A town-centre practice, based in health centre premises, was experiencing severe pressure in terms of waiting time for appointments. The receptionists had been asked to try and achieve the Patient's Charter suggestion of patients seeing a named doctor within 24 hours. However, as they pointed out, there were never any appointments available and, apart from 'emergencies', no-one* was being seen within 24 hours. The practice had no chance of implementing the required standard.

## Our approach

The key result areas that the practice was trying to set a standard for was 'accessibility'. The way in which this was being measured was the length of time it took to be offered an appointment.

Inevitably, the practice had found it impossible simply to 'graft' a Charter standard on to existing working practices. We therefore suggested they stood back from the problem, and looked, initially, at the processes involved in offering patients speedy appointments.

The first aspect was that the list size was appropriate for the number of partners, and that sufficient surgery time was, in theory, being offered. This seemd to be fairly normal, and so we looked at practice habits and behaviour.

In interviews with the staff, three key aspects became apparent. The first was that patients were given very little guidance on how to consult the doctor. This is an important part of the Charter recommendations, appropriate use of the service is vital to the interests of patients as a whole.

The second aspect was that one doctor was much more difficult to see than others. Having excluded the possibility that he was simply more popular, we looked for other reasons for the blockage. It soon became apparent that he had a charming traditional approach, which involved calling patients back routinely after six weeks or so, whether there was likely to be any clinical indication or not. The result of this was that most surgeries were booked with patients who had attended six weeks before, before any new patients were added!

The third aspect was that the receptionists, dreading patients insisting on being seen, had taken to offering everyone the first available appointment. This meant that even patients who were attending for very routine advice, and would have been quite happy to have come in two weeks' time, were automatically being offered the next available appointment. As a result, patients who felt they had to be seen in the next day or two ended up attending as 'emergencies'.

## The solution

This was a difficult one! The issues were extremely sensitive, and verged on the question of clinical judgement. We decided to begin by discussing the whole issue of call-backs with the practice partners. Not surprisingly, there were mixed views on what should be the procedure. However, the partner most likely to encourage return visits could see for himself that this was, in effect, having a detrimental effect on other patients who wished to see him – perhaps for more important conditions.

*It was quickly agreed, however, to put more emphasis on encouraging the practice to emphasize the patients' responsibilities in terms of using the services. They were not in a position to implement a full Charter, especially as they could not yet achieve the standards they wished to offer. In the interim, the advice to patients was updated offering advice on the self-management of minor illnesses, and also explaining that routine follow-up appointments in the surgery would not be given unless either the doctor, or patient, felt it necessary.*

*The third aspect, which was the easiest, was to update the receptionists training by explaining the causes of the problem to them and seeking their own views on how requests for appointments should be handled. It was agreed that, in future, they would ask the patients when they would like to attend, positively stressing that there was, for example, 'lots of availability during the week commencing 20th', at the same time adding, 'unless, of course, you feel you need an early appointment'. Surprisingly, a significant minority of patients said that there was no rush, and were quite happy to agree a future appointment to fit in with their own diary commitments.*

*As a result, there was more availability for patients who did need to be seen quickly. This combined with a more uniform approach from the doctors, and education of the patients, relieved the situation considerably. The doctors agreed that, eventually, they would aim for the absolute minimum of callbacks, but in the meanwhile, an interim target was agreed for the doctor who made the most recalls – he agreed to reduce the recalls by 20 per cent and spread the interval to ten weeks instead of six.*

### The result

*The receptionists gained control of the appointments system, there were invariably one or two 'on-the-day' appointments available for each surgery, and the whole practice appeared more organized as a result.*

### The moral

*Agreeing Key Result Areas and specifying standards is important, but they cannot simply be implemented by magic! They need to be worked at, and setting standards is always a team effort. When the Hadzor consultant team were called in to look at the problem, it was found to be caused by a number of factors, all of which needed careful consideration.*

# Next Steps

# CHAPTER 8

# Monitoring Standards and Developing a Business Plan

## Monitoring Standards

One of the most important aspects of undertaking a Total Quality Initiative is to remember that the destination is never quite reached!

Quality is an on-going concern – it needs constant review and monitoring to ensure that the original standards and targets are still appropriate, that agreed standards are being met, and to consider whether new standards need to be set in additional areas.

Monitoring ensures that good ideas about standards of service are not lost in the day to day pressure of practice life. Therefore it is important that each standard and target is the responsibility of a named person. For example, the length of time patients wait in the surgery before they see the doctor could be responsibility of the senior resceptionist. This does not mean the senior receptionist is solely responsible for the standard, however! It simply means that it is his or her responsibility to ensure that everyone is contributing appropriately.

It would be his or her job to ensure that a note was made of patients waiting over the agreed time (say 20 minutes), that the figures were collated on a regular basis, and corrective action taken, in discussion with the partners and practice manager, where appropriate.

From time to time, probably every six months or so would be appropriate, the standard itself would be considered to ensure that 20 minutes was still appropriate, or whether changed circumstances required a new target.

KEY POINT – the monitoring and review of every single standard should be the responsibility of a named person

Every single agreed standard in each area must be on someone's action list. As with the senior receptionist, this does not mean that one individual would have the sole responsibility of reaching the standard! Rather, it means that individuals would have lead or prime responsibility for keeping an eye on specific standards of service. As has been pointed out, quality relies on excellent teamwork.

## How can lead responsibility be allocated?

The most obvious way is by agreement with individuals during Individual Performance Review (IPR), when specific objectives for the forthcoming period are agreed between the member of staff and his or her immediate superior.

Mention already has been made of IPR and sample documentation is included as Appendix 3. However, it is worth reiterating again that IPR should only be introduced with great care, and after full consultation. General practices may feel it appropriate to seek further advice on this.

## Group review

Larger practices may find that organizing a small number of representatives of different sections of the practice into a 'Quality Improvement Group' is useful. The role of Quality Improvement Groups is:

- to provide an overview of all standards and targets in the practice

- to anticipate when change is needed

- to reconcile differences between individual sections or individuals, where working practices may adversely be affecting the achievement of standards of service.

In other words, they encourage individuals to specify what they need from each other (or what sections need from each other), to keep them achieving their agreed standards. This is the 'internal customer' concept, mentioned earlier.

## Developing a Business Plan

By now, it will have become apparent that ensuring quality in standards of service, such as those outlined in the Patient's Charter, is only part of a much larger picture in terms of managing an effective and successful general practice.

To attempt to introduce specific changes to individual aspects of the service whilst beneficial to certain areas, is rather like trying to complete a jigsaw puzzle without finding the corners and straight edges! In other words, general practices need a framework – a global understanding of what the practice is trying to achieve, what it reasonably *can* achieve, where it would like to be in, say five years time, and how cost-effective are its current and proposed activities.

To manage on a day-to-day basis, without this forward look, is rather like jumping on a bus without checking its destination. Even worse if the partners and practice managers are on different buses!

The business plan is the method invariably used for clarifying:

- where you are now

- where you would like to be

- how you get there.

KEY POINT – a business
plan is your route-planner
for checking direction and
progress towards your
destination

There are several ways of developing your own business plan, although a kit tailored to general practice is probably one of the easiest. Alternatives include finding someone in the practice who has a natural interest in this to take the lead, having read appropriate literature, and/or using outside consultants (preferably those with a thorough understanding of the particular needs of general practice) to develop the business plan on behalf of the practice.

The business plan covers the following areas:

1   Where are we now and how did we get here?

- a brief history of the practice – how it reached the situation it is in today

- personal and professional goals of the partners

- current services provided

- key staff

- the current SWOT analysis (strengths, weaknesses, opportunities and threats).

2   Where do we want to be in five years' time?

- the practice Mission – what, globally, is our purpose?

- the values of the practice (what do we stand for? How do we feel we should treat patients and each other?)

- how is the local population changing? What health needs will they have?

- what services will we need to provide?

- premises – location and options for development

- directions with regard to fundholding, referral patterns, services provided on site.

3 How do we get there?

- staffing resources – what and how many staff will be needed to service the activities suggested in the business plan?

- finance – how will we identify the costs of the services to be provided? How will we fund them? How will we manage them?

- interim steps – what do we need to do now, in the next twelve months, and each subsequent 12 months to achieve our five-year programme?

## *Case History 5*

*A five-partner practice came on a team-building 'away-day'. Their aim was to cement practice relationships and understand each other better.*

*Early in the proceedings, the facilitators discovered that the practice did not have a business plan. They therefore discussed the practice's intentions over the next five years, before proceeding with the team-building aspects – it is obviously easier to build a team if there is a common purpose!*

*To begin with, each of the partners said they thought they knew where they were going, and each began to describe his or her view of the future.*

*Most talked about increased services, additional responsibilities for the practice manager, and an intention to carry out more work on site if they went fundholding. The senior partner had prepared a fundholding application.*

*Within half and hour, two partners had indicated their previously private intentions of retiring early, another said she intended to go part-time and possibly job-share, and one said he wished to go part-time and spend the remainder of the week in the research department of a university! To add to the sudden change of vision, two partners said they had not really made up their mind about fundholding. All eyes were then on the practice manager to 'solve' some of these issues for them by providing continuity. At this stage, the practice manager said she was also going to retire in eight months time (at age 60)!*

### *Our approach*

*With the partners' agreement, we changed the content of the day to explore their options with regard to their business plan. Because they had not planned ahead, nor shared their views of the future, they had placed themselves in a potentially critical 'fire-fighting' situation.*

*What is certain is that events will continue to evolve whether the practice is the instigator of change or the victim of it. Proper business planning reduces the element of surprise and allows for the production of contingency plans.*

### The result

*Even in one day we were able to ensure everyone had 'put their cards on the table'. The practice agreed, having debated its Mission and Values, that (in principle, at any rate) it did wish to go fundholding. As the practice manager was going to retire, it was agreed she would undertake the initial preparation for the fund, but that the practice would replace her with a business manager to an agreed timescale.*

*Happily, the partners agreed in principle to replace the lost hours from the two partners who wished to reduce their input by appointing one new full-time partner, and an action sheet was drawn up for the planned replacement. One of the partners agreed to stay on a year longer than intended to provide continuity during the various changes.*

### The moral

*The practice was going to be very different from what some of the partners had assumed it would be in the next five years. They had made the mistake of leaping on the bus without checking its destination – and yes – they were all on different buses! If you do not specify where you are going, you are likely to end up somewhere else!*

Business planning is not just for fundholding practices – and nor is business planning purely about arrangements for fundholding – although a common mistake is to look only at those aspects needed to fulfil fundholding requirements.

As with Total Quality, business planning is not a one-off exercise. It should provide a working document – a constant reference point for monitoring the achievement of the practice aims and objectives.

# Concluding Comments

The fact that you have taken time to read this book indicates you are prepared to consider the advantages of taking a Total Quality Approach to the Patient's Charter. We hope you will enjoy the team-building that is generated amongst partners and staff by working together through the Total Quality Process.

The maximum benefits occur when the need for sound management practices, to create a positive, content workforce (positive organizational culture), is recognized, pursued and achieved, to provide the necessary receptive environment for implementing change.

Staff in general practice are usually well-motivated and hard-working, despite the tremendous pressure which characterizes a normal working-day.

By implementing Total Quality, and developing a business plan, the efforts of the whole practice team can be directed more effectively to concentrate on those activities that will achieve the optimum outcome for patients.

For further information and advice contact: – Jacqueline B. Brooks, Lead Consultant, Hadzor Health Consultants, Hadzor Court, Droitwich Spa, Worcestershire WR9 7DR; Tel: (0905) 794401.

# APPENDICES

# APPENDIX 1

## GP Services Survey*

Date _____

**None of your individual information will be released to the GP Practice**
*Please circle replies. For example, when answering the question about your age, if you are 40 years old you would circle '3':*　　　*35–44*　　　③

| Do you have a telephone at home? | How many children (17 and under) do you have at home? |
|---|---|
| YES　　1　　　　NO　　2 | None　　　　　1 |
| | 1　　　　　　2 |
| If YES, what number _____ | 2　　　　　　3 |
| | 3–4　　　　　4 |
| | 5 or more　　5 |
| *Sex/Working Status?* | |
| Male　　— working (paid)　1 | *Ages of children (at home)?* |
| 　　　　— non-working　　2 | |
| Female — working (paid)　3 | Children aged 0–4　　　1 |
| 　　　　— non-working　　4 | Children aged 5–11　　2 |
| | Children aged 12–17　3 |
| | No children at home　4 |
| *Your Age?* | |
| | *Marital Status?* |
| 18–24　1　　55–64　5 | |
| 25–34　2　　65–74　6 | |
| 35–44　3　　75+　　7 | Single　　　　　　　　　　1 |
| 45–54　4 | Married/Cohabiting　　　　2 |
| | Widowed/Divorced/Separated　3 |

Q1　(a)　What is the name of the GP/doctor you see most frequently? _____

　　(b)　How long have you been with this particular GP?

* Created by John Ardern Research, 12 Cateaton Street, Hanging Bridge, Manchester M3 1SO, Tel: 061 832 4209

| Less than 5 years | 1 | 40–59 years | 5 |
| 5–9 years | 2 | 60 or more years | 6 |
| 10–19 years | 3 | all your life | 7 |
| 20–39 years | 4 | | |

Q1 (c) How long have you been with this particular surgery/group practice (even if not the same GP)?

| Less than 5 years | 1 | 40–59 years | 5 |
| 5–9 years | 2 | 60 or more years | 6 |
| 10–19 years | 3 | all your life | 7 |
| 20–39 years | 4 | | |

(d) How long have you lived in this area?

| Less than 5 years | 1 | 40–59 years | 5 |
| 5–9 years | 2 | 60 or more years | 6 |
| 10–19 years | 3 | all your life | 7 |
| 20–39 years | 4 | | |

(e) When was the last time that you had any contact at all with the GP practice (including telephone calls or home visits)?

| Within the last month | 1 | Within the last 5 years | 6 |
| Within the last 3 months | 2 | Longer ago | 7 |
| Within the last 6 months | 3 | Never | 8 |
| Within the last 12 months | 4 | Don't know/Can't remember | 9 |
| Within the last 2 years | 5 | | |

Q2 (a) Overall how *satisfied* are you personally with the quality of service provided for you by the GPs' practice *as a whole*?

[Score out of 5]    5/5    4/5    3/5    2/5    1/5    0/5    Don't know

(b) What are you particularly satisfied with and why do you say that?

(c) Is there anything you are particularly dissatisfied with and why do you say that?

(d)   Do you have any other suggestions or ideas for improvement?

Q3   How would you rate the quality of the service provided for you by your GP doctor on the following different aspects? **Please give a score (out of 5) where 5/5 is excellent and 0/5 is unacceptable.**

| | | 5/5 | 4/5 | 3/5 | 2/5 | 1/5 | 0/5 | Don't know |
|---|---|---|---|---|---|---|---|---|
| (a) | His/her medical knowledge | 5 | 4 | 3 | 2 | 1 | 0 | DK |
| (b) | He/she always makes the right diagnosis | 5 | 4 | 3 | 2 | 1 | 0 | DK |
| (c) | Open minded to all kinds of medicine (For example, homoeopathy) | 5 | 4 | 3 | 2 | 1 | 0 | DK |
| (d) | He/she always seeks a second opinion if he/she is unsure | 5 | 4 | 3 | 2 | 1 | 0 | DK |
| (e) | He/she is always thorough | 5 | 4 | 3 | 2 | 1 | 0 | DK |
| (f) | His/her attitude towards you | 5 | 4 | 3 | 2 | 1 | 0 | DK |
| (g) | How much he/she treats you with respect as an individual | 5 | 4 | 3 | 2 | 1 | 0 | DK |
| (h) | How much you trust your doctor | 5 | 4 | 3 | 2 | 1 | 0 | DK |
| (i) | How well he/she explains things to you | 5 | 4 | 3 | 2 | 1 | 0 | DK |
| (j) | He/she always answers your questions | 5 | 4 | 3 | 2 | 1 | 0 | DK |
| (k) | He/she doesn't just rely on pills all the time | 5 | 4 | 3 | 2 | 1 | 0 | DK |
| (l) | He/she's *not* arrogant/high and mighty | 5 | 4 | 3 | 2 | 1 | 0 | DK |
| (m) | He/she always listens to what I have to say | 5 | 4 | 3 | 2 | 1 | 0 | DK |
| (n) | He/she never hurries you | 5 | 4 | 3 | 2 | 1 | 0 | DK |
| (o) | He/she is good at getting me to a specialist/hospital quickly when I need one | 5 | 4 | 3 | 2 | 1 | 0 | DK |
| (p) | He/she keeps in touch after a hospital appointment/treatment | 5 | 4 | 3 | 2 | 1 | 0 | DK |
| (q) | He/she is good with children | 5 | 4 | 3 | 2 | 1 | 0 | DK |
| (r) | He/she knows me so well | 5 | 4 | 3 | 2 | 1 | 0 | DK |
| (s) | He/she's sympathetic to even trivial aches and pains | 5 | 4 | 3 | 2 | 1 | 0 | DK |

*Now some questions about receptionists*

Q4 How would you rate the receptionist at your group practice on the following different aspects? **Please give a score (out of 5) where 5/5 is excellent and 0/5 is unacceptable.**

|     |                                          | 5/5 | 4/5 | 3/5 | 2/5 | 1/5 | 0/5 | Don't know |
|-----|------------------------------------------|-----|-----|-----|-----|-----|-----|------------|
| (a) | How easy to get through on the telephone | 5   | 4   | 3   | 2   | 1   | 0   | DK         |
| (b) | Speed of response to the telephone       | 5   | 4   | 3   | 2   | 1   | 0   | DK         |
| (c) | Attitude on the telephone                | 5   | 4   | 3   | 2   | 1   | 0   | DK         |
| (d) | Finding the most convenient appointment for you | 5 | 4 | 3 | 2 | 1 | 0 | DK       |
| (e) | Welcome to you in the surgery            | 5   | 4   | 3   | 2   | 1   | 0   | DK         |
| (f) | Overall about the receptionist           | 5   | 4   | 3   | 2   | 1   | 0   | DK         |
| (g) | System for repeat prescriptions          | 5   | 4   | 3   | 2   | 1   | 0   | DK         |

*And about the surgery itself:*

|     |                          | 5/5 | 4/5 | 3/5 | 2/5 | 1/5 | 0/5 | Don't know |
|-----|--------------------------|-----|-----|-----|-----|-----|-----|------------|
| (h) | Clear signs at the surgery | 5 | 4   | 3   | 2   | 1   | 0   | DK         |
| (i) | Relaxing waiting rooms   | 5   | 4   | 3   | 2   | 1   | 0   | DK         |
| (j) | Information provided      | 5   | 4   | 3   | 2   | 1   | 0   | DK         |
| (k) | Car parking facilities    | 5   | 4   | 3   | 2   | 1   | 0   | DK         |

*Appointments*

Q5 (a) How long do you think each appointment with the doctor is? _____ minutes.

(b) Do you feel that this is:   not long enough   1        too long        3

about right        2

(c) How long do you normally have to wait in the waiting room for your appointment (already made)? _____ minutes.

(d) Do you feel that this is:   much too long   1        about right   3

a little too long   2

(e) Should surgery be open longer hours/more days?:   Yes        1

No        2

Don't know   3

If 'Yes' when? _____

_____

Q6 (a) Which of these services do you think are currently provided by staff at this Medical Centre? (Circle responses under (A) below).

(b) Which of these have you or anyone in your family ever used (from this Medical Centre)? (Circle responses under (B) below).

(c) How would you rate *each* of these services (at this Medical Centre), whether used or not? Please give a score (out of 5) where 5/5 is excellent and 0/5 is unacceptable.

|  | (A) | (B) | 5/5 | 4/5 | 3/5 | 2/5 | 1/5 | 0/5 | Don't know |
|---|---|---|---|---|---|---|---|---|---|
| Health Visitors | 1 | 1 | 5 | 4 | 3 | 2 | 1 | 0 | DK |
| District Nurses | 2 | 2 | 5 | 4 | 3 | 2 | 1 | 0 | DK |
| Chiropodists | 3 | 3 | 5 | 4 | 3 | 2 | 1 | 0 | DK |
| Nurse advisers to the elderly | 4 | 4 | 5 | 4 | 3 | 2 | 1 | 0 | DK |
| MacMillan Nurses | 5 | 5 | 5 | 4 | 3 | 2 | 1 | 0 | DK |
| Nursing Auxiliaries | 6 | 6 | 5 | 4 | 3 | 2 | 1 | 0 | DK |
| Midwives | 7 | 7 | 5 | 4 | 3 | 2 | 1 | 0 | DK |
| Nurses at the practice | 8 | 8 | 5 | 4 | 3 | 2 | 1 | 0 | DK |

(d) How much do you think all these staff work together as a *single* operation *within* the doctor's practice at this Medical Centre?

| Completely | 1 | Not at all | 4 |
|---|---|---|---|
| Mostly | 2 | Don't Know | 5 |
| Partly | 3 | | |

*Home Visits*

Q7 (a) How would you rate home visits on the following: Please give a score (out of 5) where 5/5 is excellent and 0/5 is unacceptable.

|  | 5/5 | 4/5 | 3/5 | 2/5 | 1/5 | 0/5 | Don't know |
|---|---|---|---|---|---|---|---|
| The speed of response | 5 | 4 | 3 | 2 | 1 | 0 | DK |
| The attitude of the doctor/ receptionist when you call | 5 | 4 | 3 | 2 | 1 | 0 | DK |
| The attitude of the doctor when he/she comes | 5 | 4 | 3 | 2 | 1 | 0 | DK |

Q7 (b) Do you think that GPs/doctors should come out at night? **(Circle one code only)**

> Whenever *you* consider it necessary     1
> Only when *he/she* considers it necessary     2
> Don't know     3
> Other_____

(c) Would you mind if a GP/doctor from another surgery saw you if you were ill in an emergency at night?

> Yes, I *would* mind     1
> No, I *would not* mind     2
> No opinion either way     3

*New Ideas*

Q8 A number of new *ideas* **(stress only ideas at this stage)** are being considered by the Medical Centre. What do you think about each of these in turn?

**(5/5=Excellent Idea to 0/5=Unacceptable)**

(a) A nurses's surgery where patients could make an appointment to see the nurse instead of the doctor.

| 5/5 | 4/5 | 3/5 | 2/5 | 1/5 | 0/5 | Don't know |

Why do you say that? _____
_____

(b) A system where patients who attend surgery without an appointment are seen first by a nurse who would consult the doctor if necessary.

| 5/5 | 4/5 | 3/5 | 2/5 | 1/5 | 0/5 | Don't know |

Why do you say that? _____
_____

(c) An initial home visit being done by a nurse to assess the situation and report back to the doctor.

| 5/5 | 4/5 | 3/5 | 2/5 | 1/5 | 0/5 | Don't know |

Why do you say that? _____

_____

(d) A nurse instead of a doctor routinely visits those who are chronically sick and housebound.

| 5/5 | 4/5 | 3/5 | 2/5 | 1/5 | 0/5 | Don't know |

Why do you say that? _____

_____

(e) A 'phone-in' surgery, where patients could phone in and speak to the doctor instead of coming in for a personal consultation.

| 5/5 | 4/5 | 3/5 | 2/5 | 1/5 | 0/5 | Don't know |

Why do you say that? _____

_____

Q9  Which of these services would you particularly like to be available in your practice? Circle which ones.

| Dietary help | 1 |
| Community occupational therapy | 2 |
| Social workers | 3 |
| Family counselling services | 4 |
| Bereavement counselling | 5 |
| Stress counselling | 6 |
| Problem counselling | 7 |
| Psychologist | 8 |

# APPENDIX 2

## Health-check Phase – Semi-structured Interview

Date _____

Practice _____ No. of partners _____ List size _____

*Begin by explaining reason for interview, reassurance/all comments in confidence, etc.*

### 1. PERSONAL DETAILS    Grade _____ No. of hours per week _____

Name _____ Position _____ DoB _____
   (Dr/Mr/Mrs/Miss/Ms)

Main liaison within practice _____

Accountable to _____ Position _____

Number of staff directly responsible for _____

How long has individual been in post? _____

Previous type of employment _____

Highest educational qualification(s) obtained _____

_____

Is the interviewee's current position commensurate with education and experience?
(Ask individual to comment briefly on aspirations and career history)

_____

_____

### 2. PRACTICE BASICS

Ask the interviewee to comment on the following:

Working environment (ie physical surroundings and facilities)  _____

_____

_____

Interviewer's perception of working environment  _____

_____

_____

Main aim of practice. Is there a Mission/Statement of Intent/Values?      Yes / No*

If 'yes', does the individual know what it is?  _____

_____

## 3.  THE INDIVIDUAL IN HIS/HER WORK ENVIRONMENT
Main role of individual, and main aim of section in which he/she works. (Note: GPs' replies should be more global, relating to overall practice/health aims)

Main role of individual  _____

Aim of section/function  _____

_____

What does the individual think his or her area does best? Please describe  _____

_____

What could be done better?_____

How and why?  _____

_____

*Please delete as appropriate

Are there any Quality standards/targets which have been agreed with the individual or with the section?                Yes / No / Sort of, but not written down*

If 'yes' (or 'sort of') please describe   _____

_____

Has    the    individual    any    perception    of    his    or    her    own performance?                Yes / No*

Please comment, for example, is Individual Performance Review in place? If not, do some of the partners or practice manager give feedback?

_____

_____

## 4a.   RELATIONSHIPS WITHIN THE PRACTICE

Please describe the general atmosphere in the practice   _____

_____

_____

Are there any areas which seem to be consistently difficult or troublesome? Please describe   _____

_____

_____

Think about the other staff/sections in the practice. Could your job be made simpler, or more satisfactory by other staff/partners changing how they do things? Please describe   _____

_____

*Please delete as appropriate

97

_____

_____

What do you think works particularly well in the practice? _____

_____

_____


## 4b.  INTERNAL COMMUNICATIONS

What opportunities are there to mix with other practice staff – formally (practice meetings) or informally (social events)?

_____

_____


Do you go to   a) meetings?     Yes/No*                    b) social events?     Yes/No*

How useful do you think they are? Can the interviewee suggest anything to improve them?

_____

_____


## 5.  RELATIONSHIPS WITH OUTSIDE BODIES

Which other organizations/individuals do you have contact with, if any? (For example hospitals, FHSAs, other outside agencies)

_____


*Please delete as appropriate

What are your main commendations for and frustrations with services provided by any other bodies mentioned above?

_____

_____

If frustrations are mentioned, can the interviewee describe these, and state how they could be resolved?

_____

_____

## 6. SOME PERSONAL VIEWS

What are your main areas of satisfaction in coming into work? (ie What makes you feel good?)

_____

_____

and your main frustrations? _____

_____

If you could change three aspects of your working environment, in the widest sense, what would they be? Can you prioritize them?

1. _____

2. _____

3. _____

If only one wish, which is the most important? _____

Finally, what do you think is the public's view of the practice? What would they say was the best aspect?

_____

and the worst? _____

Do you have any additional ideas to change or improve the service? _____

_____
_____

*End – Thanks/reassurances as to purpose and when they will receive feedback on overall Health-check.*

Interviewer's own comments: _____

_____

Main problem areas for further attention _____

Action and referral to other Hadzor consultants specialist team members _____

_____ Interviewer's initials _____

# APPENDIX 3

## Individual Performance Review: Guide and Documentation for Staff in General Practice

### Notes on Administration and Clerical IPR System

The IPR System is designed for the use of general practice staff.
The purpose is:

- to provide a focus for the key work activities of individual members of staff

- to encourage people to think through personal career issues and define their development needs

- to enable the principal objectives of the general practice to be achieved in a structured and measurable manner, in consultation with the employee

- to provide clear guidelines about what job performance is expected and to give feedback about this.

The main features of the system are that, initially, the employee and the manager should jointly agree a set of objectives or working standards that will form the focus of most working activity.

At roughly quarterly intervals an informal review meeting is held between the two, at which progress and obstacles to progress are discussed. At the end of the twelve-month period, a Major Performance Review meeting is held, and on this occasion performance and achievement of objectives for the whole year are discussed and feedback given to the employee. At the same time, any personal development needs are identified and plans drawn up to deal with them. The coming year's objectives are then agreed and the cycle is repeated.

If thought necessary, the manager's manager (or partners) can become involved to ensure that the process is working properly, that the results have been assessed fairly, and to offer counselling or advice if required.

The level of objective agreed should be commensurate with the level of responsibility of the employee, and should fit in with the practice's aims and objectives as outlined in its Business Plan.

**Personal Preparation Questionnaire[1]**

## Confidential to Employee and Manager

This questionnaire is provided to help you to prepare for your Major Review Meeting. You are not required to show it to your manager unless you so wish, although it is usually helpful to share it.

**What is it about your present job that you:**

like? _____

_____

dislike? _____

_____

**What are your key job skills?** _____

_____

_____

**Do you have skills or knowledge you are not using to the full?** _____

_____

_____

**How do you work most effectively?**
**(eg to deadlines, with a particular type of manager, in a team, etc.)** _____

_____

_____

_____

[1] To be completed by individual staff, prior to Major Review Meeting

What have been the factors which may have prevented you from doing your job better?

_____

_____

Would you like a change of job and, if so, why? _____

_____

_____

Where would you like to see yourself in the next two to five years? _____

_____

_____

Does the lack of any skills or knowledge limit your progress? _____

_____

_____

What additional education, training or experience do you feel you need, either to achieve promotion or to enable you to gain more satisfaction from your present job?

_____

_____

_____

_____

_____

IPR System

## Objectives and Standards for Coming Year
**(To be agreed between employee and manager)**

Employee's Name: _____

Manager's Name: _____

Date of meeting: _____

Dates agreed for
review meetings:  1 _____  2 _____  3 _____  Major Review _____

| Action Plans and Performance Standards | Target dates |
|---|---|
|  |  |
|  |  |
|  |  |
|  |  |
|  |  |
|  |  |

**Please continue on separate sheet if necessary**

## Personal Development Plan

**(To be agreed between employee and manager)**

**Employee's name:** _____

**Manager's name:** _____

**Date of meeting:** _____

| Development Plan | Target dates |
|---|---|
|  |  |
|  |  |
|  |  |
|  |  |
|  |  |
|  |  |

**Please continue on separate sheet if necessary**

## Check-list for Major Performance Review Meeting

Before the Major Review Meeting, the manager should:

- be familiar with any previous review discussion or reports
- be familiar with the employee's objectives and standards for the year under review
- prepare for the subject headings to be discussed
- set aside adequate time – 1½ to 2 hours is usually required
- arrange a quiet place with no interruptions
- adopt an approach that helps establish standards for further action as well as reviewing previous performance.


The employee should:

- prepare for the meeting by using the Personal Preparation Form
- carry out a 'self-appraisal' of performance against the objectives and standards
- consider personal development needs.

Major Review Meeting Record

Employee's name: _____

Manager's name: _____

Date of meeting: _____

Period covered by Annual Review: _____

| Agreed plans | Comment on achievement |
|---|---|
|  |  |
|  |  |
|  |  |
|  |  |
|  |  |
|  |  |

*NB: In the first year, if plans and performance standards have not been agreed, record achievements only.*

# APPENDIX 4

## Quality Standards in Management

| Management standard | Current situation in practice (add notes) | Action to be taken | By whom? Enter name | By when? Enter date |
|---|---|---|---|---|
| Effective recruitment and induction | | | | |
| IPR (Individual Performance Review) | | | | |
| Personal Action Plans as part of IPR | | | | |
| Team briefing (systematic communciations and speedy transfer of information) | | | | |
| Mission and Values statement | | | | |
| Open and participative management style with effective delegation | | | | |

# APPENDIX 5

## Check-list for Assessing the Quality of the Practice Environment

The areas which need to be taken into consideration include the following:
(Make your own notes and make reference to the Patient's Charter).

**Entering the surgery** – ease of access, directions, how easy to find the correct consulting room, toilets, are facilities for disabled people adequate, etc?

_____

_____

**Named staff** – are _all_ staff identifiable, eg by name badges? Do they always introduce themselves to patients before beginning an interview?

_____

_____

**Reception** – is there an appropriate degree of privacy for patients? How tidy are the areas visible to patients?

_____

_____

**Waiting** – are the seats comfortable? Is reading material up to date and does it cater for varying interests? What is the focal point for patients who are waiting? Are the chairs in an informal layout, or in stiff rows? Are there toys to keep children occupied?

_____

_____

**Notices** – are they properly produced, typed, or printed, or is there evidence of scraps of paper, yellowing sellotape, and handwritten efforts? Are the words 'please' and 'thank you' in evidence, or could the notices be called abrupt?

_____

_____

**Background noise** – is there a separate play area for children? Is there appropriate background music, or does the sound of ringing telephones dominate the practice?

_____

_____

**Furnishings** – are the colours co-ordinated – does it appear that there was a plan when the rooms were arranged, or do they seem to be furnished with unco-ordinated cast-offs?

_____

_____

**If there is a branch surgery** – is the standard of furnishings and equipment equivalent to those in the main surgery, or does it seem like the poor relation?

_____

_____

**Lighting** –is it too harsh, or too dark? Would softer lighting – dimmer switches, spot-lights, or desk or table lights – allow more flexible and appropriate lighting effects?

_____

_____

**Finishing touches** – are there pictures, and/or an arrangement of dried or fresh flowers on the reception desk?

_____

_____

_____

**Colour** – is there a dominant theme, or would it be difficult to describe the colour 'scheme' in your surgery? What could be done with minimal cost to provide a more definite effect? Are the colours suitable for the purpose?

Most people know that green is considered to be restful, blue cold, and that red is not generally conducive to helping patients relax! However, small splashes of colour, within an overall theme, can add interest to the surroundings.

*Note:* *One range of colours which can be used most successfully are those in the peach shades – from pale almond to brick red or cinnamon, as they are warm, cheerful, and are believed to have an uplifting effect – similar to red, but without the disadvantages.*

*If you are not happy with the colour schemes once you have assessed these, it may be worth experimenting with small touches of this range, before embarking on a more ambitious project.*

# APPENDIX 6A

## The Appointments Questionnaire (Partners)

### Appointments – In House

What do you require from an appointment system? Please describe briefly.

_____

_____

Do you require an even workload of patients morning and afternoon?          Yes/No*

*or*

Do you prefer to hold more consultations:          Morning/Afternoon*

Would you like a daily status check on patient appointment availability times?
Yes/No*          Please comment.

_____

_____

Will you bring appointment times forward in the afternoon to accommodate more appointments?          Yes/No*          Please comment:

_____

_____

Do you prefer to offer more appointments at the end of (tick as appropriate)

a) Morning surgery ☐          b) Evening surgery ☐          c) Neither ☐

d) Alternative ☐          Please comment _____

* Please delete as appropriate

What is your ideal start time?

_____

What is your ideal finish time? _____

Do you use your computer during consultations?        Yes/No*

Does this: (please tick)       a)   take extra time? ☐       b)   save time? ☐

How much time does it:       a)   take? _____       b)   save? _____

What monitoring of appointments has already been undertaken, if any? (Please describe)

_____

_____

How is the practice nurse's time being adapted to cope with health promotion clinics, etc? (Please comment)

_____

_____

Would you prefer to see a personal list only        Yes/No*

Would you prefer a weekly appointment of all surgery activities instead of daily diary sheets?       Yes/No*

Other comments: _____

_____

_____

*Please delete as appropriate

# APPENDIX 6B

## Patients' Views on Appointments

We should be very grateful if you would spare us a few minutes to give your views on our services. This will help us to see what improvements should be made.

Do you prefer to see your personal family doctor: (please tick)

a)  Each time you visit? ☐          b)  It's not important ☐

Do the appointment times suit you?          Yes/No*          If 'No' please explain

_____

_____

How difficult is it for you to book an appointment for routine matters? Please comment on your experiences.

_____

_____

How difficult is it for you to book an urgent appointment? Please comment.

_____

_____

What changes, if any, would you like to make to the present appointment system? Please describe.

_____

_____

_____

* Please delete as appropriate

Are you aware of all the services your family doctor can provide? (Please tick)

a) Yes ☐     b) No ☐     c) Not sure ☐

d) Have not had information leaflet ☐

What extra services would you like to see, if any? Please comment.

_____

_____

_____

What do you think are the most pleasing aspects of the surgery? Please describe.

_____

_____

_____

Any other comments? _____

_____

_____

_____

*This questionnaire is in strict confidence and patient identity is not required.*
*Thank you very much for your participation.*

# APPENDIX 7

## Carrying out a Survey
(Extract from the Patient's Charter: technical guidance on monitoring)
### Sample size

The appropriate sample size will depend on two factors: the expected value of the percentage to be estimated (ie the portfolio of patients whom you believe are receiving the Charter standard) and the level of precision which is required (since no sample can be guaranteed to give the exact 'true' figure for all patients).

The further the expected value is from 50 per cent, the more clear cut is the balance between successes and failures to meet Charter standards, and the smaller the sample size necessary to achieve a particular level of precision. On the other hand, the greater the level of precision required, the larger the sample must be.

To obtain an estimate likely to be within at most one percentage point of the true figure, the sample must be four times as large as that necessary to achieve a precision of plus or minus two percentage points.

Table X provides examples of the sample sizes needed to achieve different levels of precision for specific expected success rates.

| Expected success rate (%) | Required precision (% points) | | |
| --- | --- | --- | --- |
| | +/–1% | +/–2% | +/–5% |
| 95 | 1900 | 500 | 100 |
| 90 | 3600 | 900 | 150 |
| 75 | 7500 | 1900 | 300 |
| 50 | 10 000 | 2500 | 400 |

**Table X**: Sample size (rounded to nearest 50)

The precision required for central returns is plus or minus 5%, or better, but local requirements may differ from this.

### Sample selection

It is vital that the patients selected are broadly representative of the full range of patients normally treated, and of the full range of their experiences. For example, immediate assessment in accident and emergency departments will need to be monitored at different times of the day and night, and on different days of the week. However, the number of patients sampled at each occasion should be in proportion to the number normally seen. Otherwise, too much weight will be attached to the experience of relatively few patients. Waiting times in out-patient clinics will need to be monitored both early and later, as well as covering both 'good' and 'bad' clinics. Monitoring respect for privacy, dignity and religious and cultural beliefs must cover the full range of patients by age, sex and ethnic origin.

# INDEX

Lightning Source UK Ltd.
Milton Keynes UK

175985UK00001B/3/P